Science Returns to God

SCIENCE
RETURNS
TO GOD

by
JAMES H. JAUNCEY

ZONDERVAN PUBLISHING HOUSE
GRAND RAPIDS   MICHIGAN

Second printing of paperback edition April 1971

Third printing   October 1971
Fourth printing February 1972

Library of Congress Catalog Card No. 61-14869

ACKNOWLEDGMENT

I wish to acknowledge very gratefully the help received from Dr. John N. Moore, of Michigan State University, who has carefully reviewed the original work and offered his kind suggestions, many of which have been incorporated in this revision.

CONTENTS

FOREWORD

Publication of this book is "good news" to those counting the increasing number of available creationist books, which became significant nationally in the 1960's and is continuing to enlarge in this new decade.

James Jauncey provides cogent reasons why scientists are returning to God, and turning to the Holy Bible for answers to age-old questions about origins. In his Introduction he reviews recent changes in modern technology that have caused some scientists to become greatly concerned about their social responsibilities. He touches upon space travel, population growth, nuclear energy, and electronics.

Sensing the growing dilemma of citizens of the modern scientific age who are also committed to the Christian faith, the author shows in his first main chapter that an armistice is in order between the development of science and religious concepts. He explores with the reader new dimensions of the historical conflict between proponents of science and religion. If one accepts the premise that *valid* insights cannot be destroyed in any discipline of man, then truth in one field of study can only illumine truth in another field. In discussing the impact of research findings of geologists, biologists, physicists and psychologists, Jauncey successfully avoids rationalizations that might appear to bring about harmony on points that cannot now be harmonized, and he shows that extrapolations by scientists into philosophical areas must be recognized as such.

In Chapters Two and Three the author writes of the science of the Bible and gives attention to the supernatural. He takes the traditional or conservative position "that the Bible in its entirety is the Word of God," and handles very fairly the extreme position of some critics. Especially noteworthy is his discussion of miracles and scientific laws. He points out that God, the Author of all laws, could have and maybe does manipulate laws and alter the rate of natural processes without actually breaking any laws. The author's deep conviction about the reliability of the Scriptures is rewarding to read.

In three chapters the author develops his ideas on antiquity, origins, and use of ancient records by archae- ologists. In Chapter Four he notes some of the difficul- ties of radioactive dating and study of plant and animal fossils. In Chapter Five the intriguing question of ori- gins is explored. He treats well the theory of evolution and brings to the reader's attention serious problems relating to natural selection and mutations.

He maintains most appropriately that the study of heredity, or genetics, cannot be used with any real success to support the theory of evolution. Plants and animals, in general, produce offspring much like the parents in generation after generation. Therefore, there is great truth in the assertion that "fixity of kinds" can be demonstrated, which is wonderfully in accord with "after its kind" as found ten times in Genesis 1. Much to the benefit of the reader, the author recog- nizes that mutations are changes of already existing genes, but do not give rise to new genes for new traits. Appearance of new traits would be required if supposed transmutations from one kind to another kind of plant or animal were to occur as claimed by evolutionists.

Christian readers should be greatly encouraged to find Jauncey supporting the Word of God as the one and only source of unchanging answers about origins, such as he lists: origin of the universe, the earth, life, man, and man's culture. Many men in various scientific fields have ideas about such origins but the author holds quite correctly that the ideas of men about origins are only speculative, and are not open to any possible test according to accepted scientific methods. No man can study scientifically the cosmic past.

In his excellent Chapter Six Jauncey analyzes numerous problem areas or apparent difficulties in the Bible. He touches upon the subjects of Cain's wife, longevity of people, causes and extent of Noah's Flood, tower of Babel, destruction of Sodom and Gomorrah, Lot's wife, plagues of Egypt, crossing of the Red Sea and the River Jordan, Joshua's long day, miracles, and events in the life of Jesus Christ. He concludes that "it is helpful to note that there is nothing in these incidents which is contrary to science even though there is much (as we can expect) which is *beyond* science."

After an informative chapter on "last things" and another on consideration of psychological aspects of the Christian experience and conversion, Jauncey concludes this book with a look to the future. Upon reminding the reader that "increasing scientific knowledge has brought about great vindication and understanding of the Christian position" and interpretation of reality, he poses what might be expected in nuclear physics, astronomy, dating methods, mathematics, evolutionary thought, origin of man and life, archaeology, and psychology.

This is a hopeful book that is helpful in strengthening Christian belief. Such possible edification of the faithful is highly commendable. And this book is definitely recommended reading for anyone who is concerned about relationships of the truths of the Bible to the truths of different fields of science.

— John N. Moore, M. S., Ed. D.
Professor of Natural Science
Michigan State University

INTRODUCTION

The Scientific Revolution

The evidences are piling up that we are in the midst of the greatest revolution in human living since the Renaissance. This is due to the tremendous explosion in scientific knowledge which has been occurring within the last few decades. Even for those of us who have been close to the frontiers of science all our lives, it is hard to believe what is happening. When some of us were in school about a quarter of a century ago, there were things that seemed to us would not develop for five hundred years or more, but which have now occurred within our own lifetime. The reason for all this is that the necessities of war have spurred on scientific effort with an abundance of funds at its disposal, so that there has been literally a snowballing of invention. These discoveries of recent years have been interrelated into the various fields of science, one feeding the other and so on, thus multiplying the total effect.

To the scientist of today, scientific discovery is like a vehicle of tremendous proportions which, without brakes or other controls, has started on its journey down an incline. Even if we wanted to — and we do not — we could do nothing to stop its gathering momentum. But it is obvious that disaster lies ahead unless mankind gets into the driver's seat and gets things under control.

Scientists throughout the world today are largely frightened men. This does not mean that they are unduly pessimistic. It does mean that they are fully aware of the dangers that are facing civilization. Most of them have the confidence that mankind will find a way of getting things under control before it is too late. This is the major reason why so many scientists are returning to God as a final and only answer to the problems of the world.

A curious thing about this scientific revolution is that with almost every development which promises untold good for the human race there is also a correspondingly tremendous possibility of peril. It must be heartbreaking to God to see that, as He permits men to unlock the secrets of the universe for the benefit of mankind, mankind threatens his own destruction by the use of these gifts.

The most exciting of all the scientific developments in recent years has been in the space field. This has been largely due to the guided missile program which has been accelerated because of the dangers of the cold war. It is now apparent that within our lifetime men may make journeys beyond the moon to Mars, and other planets on our particular fringes of outer space. This will open up to the world new vistas of adventure and expansion comparable only to the discovery of the Americas in 1492.

This development could easily be the answer, in the goodness of God, to the critical problems which are facing us upon this earth because of the population explosion. History has shown that when mankind faces a new kind of need, there is always a provision for that need. It is difficult to tell at this stage what the conquest of our part of the solar system is going to mean for us, but certainly it means that many of the natural resources of these heavenly bodies may come to be at the disposal of man when he is facing serious depletion of his own resources.

It could also be that the discoveries in space will give hope for colonization to the millions of the future for whom the earth could become too crowded. At the moment, there appear to be serious problems about human beings living on the moon or the planets, but it is not inconceivable that developments in engineering can solve these. In any case, the opening up of space promises great good for the future of mankind.

On the other hand, these discoveries also carry the threat of tremendous peril. If any nation or individual with evil intentions could find a vantage point, either by an artificial satellite in orbit, or on the moon, or one of the planets, it is clear he could hold the whole earth to ransom. So fearful would be the threat that he could issue from such a vantage point, that the nations of the earth would be faced with either surrender or total destruction. This is one of the reasons why space men in this country are so anxious that we should keep up with Russia in space developments. The winner of the race will not only gain prestige, but he could easily conquer the world and have in his hands the destinies of the future. Thus this great good which God is giving to us in our own day is being fraught with terrible peril.

Another development which is going to change our lives beyond all recognition is the discovery of nuclear energy. In most people's minds, this is largely related to the development of the atomic and hydrogen bombs, but to the scientist it means the unlocking of power in quantities never before available on this earth.

Until now, apart from natural power, the most significant source of power has come from chemical means, which is finally dependent upon the motion of electrons. Nuclear power, on the other hand, comes from the very heart of the atom and is infinitely greater than chemical power.

Nuclear power becomes available because of a curious freak of nature. It just so happens that when you smash the nucleus of a heavy atom, like uranium, the total mass of the parts is less than the mass of the original. Since mass cannot be lost, it is transferred into energy. By another curious fact, the multiplying factor when this occurs is infinitely large. In the metric system, one unit of mass is multiplied by 9 times 100 billion billion in producing nuclear energy. This is a direct result of Einstein's famous equation, $E = mc^2$. For the average man uninterested in higher mathematics, it means simply that a very small amount of mass can produce an enormous quantity of energy. When this transference of mass into energy is uncontrolled, it happens in the fraction of a microsecond (millionth of a second) and in so doing creates an enormous explosion. If its liberation can be controlled, then it means that power for useful purposes is available.

The fusion process is similar, except that it happens somewhat in reverse. If we take two hydrogen nuclei and fuse them together, it so happens that the mass of the combination is less than the total mass of the original constituent parts. This mass is once again transferred into energy. If this happens without control, you have the hydrogen bomb. Some idea of the power of this fearful explosion is shown by the fact that in the Pacific experiments, an island three miles long by one mile wide disappeared entirely. Scientists have known of the possibility of fusion for many years. But they did not have a source of heat sufficiently high to bring it about. The atomic explosion provided this.

For years now scientists have been giving their attention to finding ways and means by which the power released by fission and fusion can be so under control that it can be used for human benefit. Successes have already been registered. There are cities now which are lit by nuclear power. Nuclear submarines roam the seas. This holds great promise for mankind, particularly in the light of the depletion of natural resources of power such as coal and petroleum. Especially in the case of nuclear energy by fusion, the raw materials necessary exist in such tremendous quantities in the world that there will be no shortage for millions of years. Thus it seems again that at the time when man's increasing need for further sources of power is beginning to be felt, God is allowing men to unlock the secrets of the power of the universe. Many countries at the moment which are unpopulated and unproductive because they do not have ready sources of power will blossom like a rose when this marvelous new source of power becomes available to them.

But along with this evidence of God's smile on mankind, there are also fearful evidences of danger. They tell us that, at the time of this writing, one jet bomber can bring about more destruction on one mission than has been brought about so far by every other war plane in the history of the world. But even this is nothing to be compared with the fearful weapons now on the drawing boards.

Less than a century ago, Thomas Edison noticed a curious effect which to him did not seem to have any practical value. He noted that in a vacuum, electrons had a one way motion from one electrode to another. This apparently insignificant effect has ushered in the tremendous world of electronics. From it we have had radio, television, radar, computers, and a host of other developments. These have been so great that the whole face of business and industrial life has been changed. Much of the drudgery of monotonous processes is now taken over by machines by the help of electronics.

Probably the most fascinating of these are the computers, or electronic brains. Many of these are capable of doing in a few seconds that which it would take a team of brilliant mathematicians many years to do. As a matter of fact, both in war and in peace, design engineers are seeking to replace the human element by computers, because the human brain is neither accurate nor quick enough for the demands of the future. There are some who are even suggesting that the driver of an automobile be replaced by an electronic brain because the complex problems of traffic are becoming too involved for the human brain to negotiate.

The discoveries in electronics promise to make man's life happier and better in an infinite number of ways. Many of the dangers of life will be removed. Much of the drudgery will disappear and he will be able to give his attention to more creative things. It has already made a tremendous contribution to his recreational and leisure life. In every way, electronics is one of God's greatest gifts.

But once again we see this curious parallel of good and evil, because electronics also poses a threat. One of the problems of law enforcement in America for a long time has been the genius of the criminal which has enabled him to rule vast crime empires and yet remain untouched by the law for many years. Just imagine what could happen if these evil men were to have at their disposal the electronic brain and other developments of electronics! Many discoveries of science in this direction are going to be a tremendous bonanza for them and, because of this, greatly increased peril for the social life of mankind.

Especially since World War II, we can point with justifiable pride to the tremendous developments in the related fields in chemistry, biology, and medicine. By these joint efforts, diseases which once exercised a terrible threat to mankind have completely disappeared. Some of us can remember in our childhood the danger of diphtheria every winter. We saw whole families wiped out by this fearful destroyer. Today this disease is very rare.

Those of us who have children were thrilled a few years ago with the development of the Salk vaccine. Every year we dreaded the onset of summer because of the threat that it held to our children because of polio. Now this dreadful disease is being forced to exit.

Developments are continuing with regard to cancer. Some cancers already seem to be under control. It is not unreasonable to assume that within our own lifetime this nightmare disease will also become a thing of the past.

These are only a few of the developments in our time. The new drugs and the new techniques in surgery have expanded man's life enormously. As a matter of fact, this is the major factor in the present population explosion.

At first sight, this appears to be all good. But it is not so. Wherever you have the possibility of good, you also have the threat of evil. This came into clear relief in the announcement that was made in January, 1960, that an English scientist had produced a liquid which, although fatal to the human body, could not be detected by taste, smell, or sight. If placed in a drink, it would bring death in twenty minutes, yet the cause of death would not be obvious in the autopsy. "The perfect murder weapon," he called it.

Many of us have been expecting this kind of discovery for many years, with the awful threat that it contains. During the Korean War, there was a great to-do by the Russians and the Chinese about the so-called "germ warfare." They knew, of course, that we were not using any such thing. They also knew that we could. Apparently, their campaign was a build-up of public opinion so that we would be prevented from using such a terrible weapon. The fact is that this kind of warfare is always a possibility; therefore, the discoveries in these related fields are by no means all benefit to mankind.

It is obvious that the world of the future is going to be overwhelmingly scientific. Not only does this face mankind with the kind of immediate danger that has been previously described, but also with the peril that, with the obtrusiveness of science, the cultural and spiritual values will be overwhelmed. If this happens, the human race has no future at all. Sooner or later man would destroy himself by his own devices. But once again we see God bending down to meet the need. With the great scientific discoveries, there has also been a tremendous resurgence in religious interest. People have been flocking to our churches as never before, with hungry hearts in search of spiritual values. Apparently God is giving us this opportunity so that we can do something about the factor of human sin in human lives, which is the basic threat to human survival. In other words, Christ is the answer.

This challenge is also related to the threat of communism. In recent years we have seen this great mass of fanatically dedicated people take over the great discoveries of science and threaten the very annihilation of civilization as we know it. Many people feel that our way of life is in greater danger now than it has ever been in the history of the world. Since America has the leadership in world affairs, she must constantly develop even the most fearful weapons, so that the communists will not dare to attack. But there is a need which is greater than this and that is that the heart of the nation should become strong. The only way in which this can occur is through a vital religious faith.

As the star of science ascends in the heavens of our lives, it is obvious that every other area of human endeavor is going to be challenged by its successes. This will be especially true in the case of religion. Unless the tenets of religious faith can survive its penetrating glare, then necessarily religion will be a dying force, and with its decay will come the end of the race.

We can be very grateful that in this day of crisis, much of the disharmony between science and religion is disappearing. The very advances of science have been conducive to a religious faith. However, there is a tremendous challenge to the Christian Church to present Christianity in such a way that it can capture the imagination and conviction of the scientific mind. That is the purpose of this book.

Chapter One

The Reconciliation

It is now some thirty years since I was in under-graduate school. During that time, I have remained fairly close to developments in science; yet I never cease to be amazed at the tremendous change in outlook during this period. When I was in school, the general outlook of scientific people was frankly hostile to religion. As a matter of fact, it was frequently pointed out that unless the young student abandoned these religious superstitions, he could not hope to progress in scientific achievement.

Now the situation is entirely different. The atheist or the hostile agnostic, even in scientific circles, is becoming a rare bird indeed. For a number of years I have been receiving invitations to speak on religion and science on many campuses throughout the land. The general attitude is always sympathetic and often very devout. This extends not only to the belief in God but also to belief in the Bible.

A couple of years ago I had occasion to make a trip with a number of missile engineers and scientists. In course of conversation, the question of the Bible came up. One outstanding scientist made the remark that he had learned not to sell the Bible short. Among that group of men, there was no negative criticism at all. As a matter of fact, they seemed to consider skepticism to be rather stupid.

Some years ago *Collier's* magazine sent a reporter on a quest which was called "A Reporter in Search of God." His researches were published in a number of articles in that magazine and subsequently incorporated in a book. Mr. Whitman, the author, found in his talks with the top scientists of this country that most of them found no difficulty at all with belief in God. Some of them admitted that in their earlier days they had been inclined to be skeptical, but with increased experience, religious conviction had deepened.[1]

Professor Millikan has also found the same thing. He states that the incidence of religious belief among scientists is certainly not less than that of the population generally and might even be more.[2] This is borne out by a visit to any college town. You find members of the scientific faculty active in the work of the local church.

In the same book he states: "... the most outstanding scientists have frequently been men who were closely identified with religious organizations, constituting at least presumptive evidence that there is no essential conflict. . . ."[3]

Dr. A. Rendle Short, who himself was an anatomist of no mean repute and who wrote a very useful book called *Modern Discovery and the Bible,* was of the opinion that much of the idea that scientists are atheistic has been due to the outspokenness of a few very radical scientists, such as Huxley, Tyndall, and Haeckel. These were not, and are not, at all representative.[4]

Further evidence of this nature is supported by the general increases in religious belief. In the last few years, church membership has increased tremendously

[1]Howard Whitman, *A Reporter in Search of God* (Garden City, New York: Doubleday and Co. Inc., 1953), p. 43.
[2]Robert Andrew Millikan, *Evolution in Science and Religion* (New Haven: Yale University Press, 1935), p. 5.
[3]*Ibid.*
[4]A. Rendle Short, *Modern Discovery and the Bible* (Chicago: Inter-Varsity Press, 1955), p. 15.

in the U.S.A. and the significance of this increase is that it is occurring at the same time as the rapid rise in scientific knowledge and education among the general population. It is obvious that people are finding no serious conflict.

Much has been said about the historical conflict between science and religion. Certainly there was a time when it seemed almost impossible to be a scientist and a Christian. This kind of conflict is disappearing. It may be worthwhile to investigate why.

Although there has been some conflict between science and religion for centuries, the problem did not come out into clear relief until the end of the eighteenth century and the beginning of the nineteenth. That was the time when the new geological discoveries were being made. It soon became possible that instead of an earth 6000 years old, as it had been generally believed, it could have gone back millions of years. This seemed to many people a direct challenge to the Biblical message.

As we see it now, this point of conflict was rather unnecessary. Most of it was due to the rather unfortunate researches of an Irish archbishop named Ussher in the seventeenth century. Apparently he was also an amateur mathematician. As the result of his calculations, he concluded that creation occurred in 4004 B. C. Since he was an archbishop, most Christian people assumed that he must be correct. The date soon appeared in the margins of Bibles and still exists in many Bibles today.

The Bible makes no such stipulation. It simply says that "in the beginning God created the heavens and the earth."[5] According to this it could just as easily have been millions of years ago as just a few thousand years ago. You can see that the problem was science versus Ussher rather than science versus the Bible. The point no longer raises serious difficulty.

[5]Genesis 1:1.

However, the greatest storm of all did not break until 1859 when Darwin published his *Origin of Species*. Although Darwin himself was not an atheist and actually stated that the Creator had breathed life into the few primary forms that he thought responsible for the natural world,[6] to most people it seemed that the new theory did away with the need for God altogether. Man appeared to be merely the product of a natural process. Atheists and those hostile to religion were quick to take up the theory of evolution and use it as a weapon against Christianity. For a hundred years this battle has raged.

However, there is evidence on every hand that the conflict seems to be disappearing. There are a great number of biologists who at least tentatively believe in evolution, but who nevertheless are active members of Christian churches and find no problem at all. The general attitude is that even if evolution were proved to be true, instead of making God unnecessary, it would merely show that this was the method God used. As we will see in a later chapter, there are many things about the theory of evolution which are open to serious doubt on scientific grounds, but there are not too many that raise the quarrel on religious grounds. The adequacy of the theory of evolution to explain the living universe is something that must be solved by the biologists themselves. The hurling of "proof texts" at them is not going to help.

Towards the end of the nineteenth century there was a great surge of discoveries in physics. It looked as if physical laws such as those of cause and effect would soon explore the universe exhaustively and express it in scientific terms. The great successes that followed one another increased people's confidence in science to such an extent that they became increasingly skeptical of anything that seemed contrary to it. This was especially true with regard to miracles. Many scientists said cate-

[6]Charles Darwin, *The Origin of Species*, Chapter XV, last paragraph.

gorically that miracles just could not happen because they had no place in the laws of cause and effect.

Since then, physics has become increasingly humble. We realize now that instead of exhausting the knowledge of the universe, we are only on the fringe. Apparently miraculous things are occurring all the time, and apparent contradictions are as frequent in physics, if not more so, than they are in religion. Faced with the mystery of the universe, the modern physicist apparently has little difficulty in accepting the difficulties of the spiritual world.

This present century started with renewed interest in psychology. With the developments of psychoanalysis and behaviorism, it seemed that even the experiences of men could be explained on psychological terms. This was a severe shock to Christian thought. It seemed to do away with the need of God even in the spiritual world. However, since then it has become increasingly obvious that explaining spiritual or psychological processes does not mean explaining them away. All that the new science can do is investigate the various channels which God Himself might choose to use. Psychology can give no real answer to the question of God. In investigations reported in the book mentioned above, Mr. Whitman has found that there is no serious conflict, generally speaking, between psychiatry and religion.[7] As a matter of fact, some years ago Dr. Jung, one of the greatest psychoanalysts of all time, expressed his conviction of the need for religion in bringing about proper adjustment.[8]

It can be seen from these considerations that there has been a gradual convergence in thought between science and religion. To say that there are no longer points of apparent conflict would be to underestimate the problem, but the harmony that has been achieved and the trend to convergence strongly suggest

[7]Op. cit., Chapter 4.
[8]C. G. Jung, Modern Man in Search of a Soul (New York: Harcourt Brace, 1933), p. 264.

that we can hope for greater unity in the future. In any case there is no longer any valid reason why the scientist cannot believe in God or the Bible, or why a religious person may be apprehensive of scientific discovery.

This is obviously as it ought to be. Intrinsically, there is nothing mutually contradictory about scientific and religious thought. Both science and revelation in the long run come from the one God. Consequently, increasing accuracy in thought and discovery must increasingly show that they are one. The problems of the past are largely due to incomplete knowledge. Science is changing all the time as it seeks to adjust itself to deeper and more accurate laws. Also in the case of religion, especially the Bible, research in the original languages and the light that has been brought to bear by archaeology have helped towards a better interpretation of truth.

To expect complete harmony between science and religion would be unrealistic, for it would entail perfect knowledge in both fields. However, the increasing convergence which has occurred with increasing knowledge shows that no insuperable problem any longer exists.

Points of difficulty in certain areas still remain, as successive chapters indicate, but these are no greater than those existing between various sciences. The sincere Christian who approaches them with an unbiased mind will find no insuperable hurdles.

CHAPTER TWO

The Science of the Bible

A great deal of the literature on science and religion deals with theism (belief in God) only. However, this does not go far enough. The average Christian finds himself involved in many other articles of faith as well. In Protestantism, these are ultimately based on the Bible, so inevitably the problem resolves into the relation between science and the Holy Scriptures.

Any consideration of the science of the Bible must inevitably depend a great deal upon one's interpretation of the Bible. Of course, the decision as to what interpretation of the Scriptures a person will follow cannot primarily be dependent upon scientific considerations. In the long run, the decisions will be upon religious grounds. However, it can be said here that there is nothing in science which is intrinsically opposed to even the most conservative view of Biblical interpretation.

To simplify matters, it can be said that there are primarily three views on the interpretation of the Bible.

First of all, there is the *traditional,* or conservative, view, which claims that the Bible in its entirety is the Word of God and, as such, is accurate in everything that it says in every branch of knowledge, including science and history. This is the position of the writer of this book.

Then there is the *radical* view which assumes that God had little or nothing to do with the Bible. Under this view, the Bible is one book among others, with its inspiration differing only in degree from the inspiration that you might get from Tennyson, Emerson, or any other writer.

Finally, there is a kind of *moderating* view which states that the Bible is primarily a textbook of religion and therefore only its religion is authoritative, but its science and history can be dismissed as legendary or fictional.

It is the point of view of the present writer that if the term "Christian" means what it says, then the criterion by which one decides which of these views of the Bible is correct must be that which Christ Himself held. What is most reasonable to us on other grounds or what would bring the least difficulties with science is quite immaterial. If a person is not prepared to base his faith on Christ, he has no faith worth defending anyhow.

It is almost universally admitted that Jesus Christ held the traditional, or conservative, view. A few examples will suffice.

He based His teaching about marriage on the factualness of the story of Adam and Eve. In Matthew 19:4, 5 He says, "Have ye not read, that he which made them at the beginning made them male and female, and said, For this cause shall a man leave father and mother and shall cleave to his wife: and they twain shall be one flesh?" referring to Genesis 2:24. The context shows that He was assuming these words to be authoritative. Mark 10:6-8 repeats this exact emphasis.

In Mark 7:13 He calls the Mosaic command to honor father and mother "the word of God." In Matthew 22:43 He refers to a psalm of David as being spoken by the Holy Ghost. In John 13:18 He is emphatic that the Scripture (that is, the Old Testament) *must* be fulfilled. In John 10:35 He says, "...The scripture cannot be broken." In Matthew 5:18 He states, "For verily I say unto you, Till heaven and earth pass, one jot or one tittle shall in no wise pass from the law, till all be fulfilled." (The "law" is the "Torah," or Five Books of Moses. The "jot" and "tittle" are insignificant parts of the Hebrew lettering.)

There can be no doubt that to Jesus the Old Testament in its entirety was the Word of God and it as such must be accepted without question.

Attempts have been made by some to assail the fortress of these categorical statements by suggesting that, since Jesus was man as well as God, He was influenced by the primitive and fallacious knowledge of His times; therefore, only His religious message needs to be taken seriously. However, if it be admitted that He was subject to error at all, there could be no retreat from the attack upon His religious veracity as well. Religion, science, and history are not separate branches of knowledge but simply rough classifications we use for our own convenience. For instance, the account of the resurrection of Jesus involves religion, science, and history, depending upon how you look at it. Take away any one aspect, and the whole thing falls to pieces. Also, if you feel that His science and history are unreliable because of the limitations of His age, why not also His religion?

Christ claimed again and again that His teaching came from God. For instance in John 8:26, He says, ". . . he that sent me is true; and I speak to the world those things which I have heard of him." Also, in John 8:28 He states, ". . . ye shall know . . . that I do nothing of myself; but as my Father hath taught me, I speak these things." A careful reading of His words, especially those in the Gospel of John, will show that He emphatically claimed divine authority for His statements.

The teaching of Christianity has constantly maintained that Jesus was God in human flesh. He Himself said (as recorded in John 14:9, 10), ". . . he that hath seen me hath seen the Father; . . . Believest thou not that I am in the Father, and the Father in me? the words that I speak unto you I speak not of myself: but the Father that dwelleth in me." Paul, in I Timothy 3:16, wrote concerning Jesus: ". . . God was manifest in the flesh . . ."

In view of this, it is difficult to escape from the position that His word is final on every aspect of knowledge upon which He speaks. Placing one's faith upon His words gives a rock under the feet, whereas otherwise one is constantly subject to the shifting sands of varying opinions.

The conservative view is also substantiated by the fact that it is the traditional view. It has stood the test of acceptance by Spirit-filled believers for centuries. No doubt of any significance has been expressed until modern times, and not even now by the majority of believers.

The most extreme position claimed that the Bible itself could be abandoned because it is not necessary to the Christian religion. The basis of faith and conduct, it was thought under this view, lay in man's own thoughts and in his own conscience. The Bible merely contained records of people's spiritual experiences and gave an insight into their views, but we in this day are no more bound by these opinions than we are by the science of the ancient Greeks.

It was true that this was a position with which many of the hostile scientists could come to terms, but not all of them. Some felt that the retreat should be carried to its logical conclusion and do away, not only with the Bible, but also with the doctrine of God. In any case, this kind of solution did not serve any useful purpose, because it left a religion so emasculated that it was very little use in personal life. There was no basis of authority and no assurance of revelation. Most of the churches which preached this message rapidly lost their congregations.

At first sight, this partition of knowledge into religious, historical, scientific and so on, which enables us to pick and choose between them instead of accepting or rejecting an area of knowledge as a whole, seems to be reasonable enough. It also is very convenient. But one wonders whether it can hold the superstructure that is put upon it.

The radical position is comparatively recent in date and is a product of lack of belief in God rather than vice versa. It is largely based on the presupposition that God cannot or does not interfere with His world; therefore, miracles, revelation, and other instances of His presence and work upon the earth cannot occur. To the Christian who is powerfully aware of the workings of God within his own life, the view will be so totally unsatisfactory that it will be given scant consideration.

The problem with the mediating view is that it seems to be "neither fish nor fowl nor good red herring." It was primarily enunciated, not as a result of study of the Bible itself, but as an attempt to come to terms with the conflict between religion and science. As has been indicated earlier, it suffers primarily from the fact that it is a view not shared by Christ. The New Testament makes it clear that He was as convinced of the science and history of the Bible as He was of its religion. Therefore, to accept this view means also to accept an unsatisfactory view on the nature of the person of Christ and His deity.

In any case, this retreat is unnecessary. Many of the greatest scientists of all time, including our own time, have been firm believers in the fact that the Bible is the Word of God. Although attempts have been made, there has been no success in trying to prove that any part of the Bible and any particular scientific truth are mutually irreconcilable. This is obvious, anyway, because of the dynamic nature of science. Science is not a body of fixed truths which are eternally true. Science is an increasing and progressive attempt to describe the truths of the universe. Its approximation to truth today may have to be abandoned tomorrow; therefore, to prove any part of the Bible to be either in harmony or disharmony with a certain scientific view is pointless. In a little while the view will have moved on; then if the attempt was to prove harmony, it will become unstuck. If the attempt was to prove disharmony, it will have lost its validity.

The fact that there are unsolved difficulties need not disturb us. There are unsolved difficulties and problems everywhere in science too. Indeed, if every difficulty in the Bible could be resolved by our human minds, this would give evidence against divine authorship. It would show that the mind of the author was no greater than the human level. Because the Bible comes from the very mind of God, much of it must always be enshrouded in difficulty and mystery.

This view that modern science can have no quarrel with the traditional view of the Bible as the Word of God does not mean that the science of the Bible is exhaustive in the fields to which it is related. The science of the Bible is mostly in embryonic form. It was not the purpose of the writers to talk about science as such, but only to elaborate to the extent to which it involved any questions on hand. What they did say was accurate enough. Modern science may elucidate and amplify the embryonic scientific statements made in the Bible.

The idea that the Bible contains scientific truth in embryo is exemplified by the story of creation. There it describes the order of creation. Not much detail is given yet this order is substantially the same as that claimed by modern geologists. The laws of hygiene given for Israel also appear to be well before their time. These and other instances of undeveloped scientific truth found in the Bible are hard to explain except on the basis of divine inspiration.

This "truth in embryo" also occurs in other areas of discussion in the Bible. In the New Testament there are very frequent references to incidents and verses in the Old Testament which take on a new and enlarged context in the New. It is also shown in our own spiritual experiences of the Bible where its passages constantly bring new truths to our hearts and minds, even though we may have been reading it for years.

In considering the scientific statements of the Bible or those which are related to science, it also must be remembered that they were written in a language and from a background which is very different from ours. Any attempts to interpret them in terms of corresponding English words or of modern viewpoints is sure to lead to error. Biblical interpretation can only be accurate as it understands what the words meant in their own particular environment.

Neither must we be too literal in our dealings with some of the imagery and some of the idioms. For instance, offence has been given to some by the reference in Joshua 10:13 that the sun stood still. It has been contended that since it is the earth that moves relative to the sun rather than the sun moving relative to the earth, then this is an obvious error. Yet we ourselves do the same. We talk about the sun rising in the morning and setting in the evening. We have a particular meaning in mind and do not intend by this to be making scientific statements about the motion of the sun. Can we expect them in ancient times to be any different?

This raises the whole question of literal versus figurative interpretation. Often the question of inspiration is said to depend on whether you interpret the Bible literally or figuratively. Now those who hold the traditional view do not deny the presence of figurative interpretation. When Christ said that He is the door, He did not mean that He is actually a physical part of a building. When it says in the book of Revelation that He is the Lamb that is slain, it does not mean in the life to come that He will appear as a dead sheep. When Peter was given the disputed keys to the kingdom, it does not mean that he was given certain pieces of metal. Also, conservatives feel that many of the incidents in the Bible which they believe to be literally true still have spiritual or figurative meaning. For instance, the history of Israel is a picture of the spiritual life of the Christian.

But this use of figurative interpretations where they seem to be justified does not mean that it is to be used as an easy way of getting out of difficulties. For instance, it is doubtful if anyone would have suggested that the story of Adam and Eve, of the Flood, or of Jonah should be interpreted figuratively if it were not for the scientific difficulties that were involved. The reason for this interpretation was simply a retreat from a difficulty.

So, how can you tell whether to take a passage figuratively or literally? The answer seems to be in the apparent intent. It is necessary to read the passage carefully and see if the writer, by his context, is advocating a figurative meaning. Then, too, the material itself may give a suggestion.

For instance, in the story of creation, the material is so detailed that it would take a great deal of ingenuity to discover figurative meanings for it all. It has been suggested that the only purpose of the creation legend (as it is called) is to strengthen belief that God is behind it all. But if this is so, why the wealth of detail? The first verse of Genesis would have been sufficient if only a figurative meaning had been intended.

Much discussion has gone on as to whether the actual words of the Bible are inspired or not. It is very difficult to see how the sentences and general meaning of the Bible can be inspired if the words are not, since words are the basis of sentences. Verbal inspiration seems to have been accepted by the New Testament writers. As we have seen, our Lord Himself said that not one jot or one tittle would be removed from the Law until all be fulfilled. Paul also, in Galatians 3:16, argues on the fact that a singular is used instead of a plural, obviously feeling that such details as these were also under the guidance of God.

But this does not mean a static view of inspiration. Although the words are inspired, the message of God is infinitely greater than any words. Right through the Bible you can find God's truth straining to be expressed to men through the human limitations of language. Constantly it goes over and beyond the words to flash on people's hearts with inspiration.

This also can be seen in the ways in which the Old Testament is quoted in the New. At first sight, the differences seem to be surprising. You would expect the quotations to be exact. Some of them, for instance, are from the Greek translation rather than from the original Hebrew Bible. However, the differences are not accidental. They are attempts by the Holy Spirit to take the basic truths of the Old Testament passage and give it amplification and meaning in its New Testament context. This often requires different words.

A person's faith in the Bible necessarily depends upon his faith in God. If God is distant and vague, happenings such as those recorded in the Bible will seem extremely strange. But those of us who have had the presence of the miracle working God in our lives for years would not be surprised at anything He might do. With Him all things are possible. Since He works inscrutably in our lives, we are not surprised that there are mysteries associated with His workings in the past. When happenings are recorded in the Bible which seem inexplicable and even apparently contradictory to well-known facts, this does not faze the devout Christian. He has seen many instances of this before, and yet in time his eyes have been opened to see underlying realities which explain it all. Perhaps this aspect of truth was best put by the apostle Paul in I Corinthians 13:12 when he said, "For now we see through a glass darkly; but then face to face. . . ."

When studying the literary characteristics of the Bible, one has to be very careful that he does not forget that primarily the Bible is a Book which God uses. Although we recognize God's inspiration of the writers, it is more important to us that He should inspire the readers. The cold, argumentative chip-on-the-shoulder attitude of many so-called fundamentalists tends to belie the message that they are trying to present. If the Bible is really inspired, it should have changed their hearts to that of love and warmth for their fellow men, rather than to hatred and unpleasantness.

The best way to look at the Bible is that it is saturated with the presence of God, and therefore any heart that goes to its pages is going to be influenced by this presence. That is why Biblical preaching has a power that cannot be found in mere ethical teaching. That is why from time immemorial we have been told to read our Bible every day. Only this way can we get an adequate sense of the power of the presence of God upon our hearts and minds.

These are areas that go far beyond science. Considerations such as those that characterize this book may strengthen our intellectual faith in Christianity and in the accuracy, authenticity, and reliability of the Word of God. But the final result must be the jump of faith which enables us to fling ourselves into the arms of God and rest there secure while the stream of changing scientific viewpoint goes by.

Chapter Three

The Supernatural

As has been mentioned in the general survey of the historical conflict between science and religion, the problem of miracle has been constantly in critical focus. Although this became almost a decisive issue through the new discoveries in physics at the end of the nineteenth century, it had been a common point of attack by atheists and freethinkers for a couple of hundred years before that. However, the earlier attacks had been from the points of view of philosophy and reason, which always appear rather intangible to the average man. Consequently, the effect was not too serious. However, when the attack against miracle shifted to the vantage point of physical science with its power of authority, its effect upon religious faith was devastating.

The standpoint of science was that nature was a "closed universe." This meant that everything within the universe was governed by an unvarying sequence of cause and effect. The universe was closed to any occurrences which deviated from this pattern. Two and two always made four. The angles at the base of an isosceles triangle were always equal. The law of gravitation was universal, etc. Whenever you had a certain combination of factors operating, the result was always the same and could not be different.

Miracles, on the other hand, could not be fitted into this framework of cause and effect. In many cases, they seemed to act contrary to the scientific laws that

33

had been established. The theologians themselves made no bones about this impasse. A miracle was usually defined as the breaking or the interruption of natural law. Consequently, the lines of conflict were very clearly drawn.

We have now reached the stage in the development of science when the closed universe idea is no longer talked about. The universe of nature is proving far too complex to be resolved into such simple terms. Even mathematical truths are no longer considered absolute in themselves but are dependent upon a set of presupposed basic truths. If you alter this foundation, the statements are no longer true.

It is similar in physics. The reign of "unalterable law" has been changed to the "evidence of probabilities." A statement in science is seldom now considered true in itself, but only within a certain limit of probability, say ninety-nine percent. This admits that instances do occur which cannot be covered by the statement concerned. This uncertainty is particularly true of the world of atomic physics where the laws of cause and effect do not operate in the same way. You cannot predict what a particular particle will do nor where it will be. All you can do is predict where it will be on the average. There is now an actual principle known as the "Principle of Uncertainty," the very name of which would cause the nineteenth century physicist to turn in his grave.

Of course, it was always stipulated by the physicist that a certain scientific law was only true under specified circumstances or conditions. This seems to be reasonable enough. Experiences with the world of nature show that there is a vast complex of conditions. Therefore to assume that a certain set of conditions is operating in any particular case is a major assumption indeed. Constantly scientists find their results upset by underlying factors which they never even dreamed were there. Therefore, even if the closed universe presupposition were strictly true, we could have no confidence that we could specify the conditions operating with sufficient accuracy to be confident of its results. This means, therefore, that the reason why a certain miracle does not harmonize with scientific knowledge may be because there were factors underlying the miracle unknown to us.

Another mistake of nineteenth century science was to assume the equivalence of scientific law with natural law. We still agree, at least within the limits of probability, that this is an orderly and not a chaotic universe. That is, it is a realm of law. Scientific study is always trying to describe this universe in terms of law so that this makes it manageable for its own purposes. It is now realized that scientific law is only the best approximation at any stage of knowledge that we can get for natural law. Scientific laws are constantly having to be revised to fit the further knowledge that is being revealed. Even such a long established law as the law of gravitation has been revised. Therefore, conflict with scientific law at any particular stage of knowledge does not necessarily mean a contradiction. Further information may easily show that it is the scientific law which was at fault.

Science itself is full of apparent inconsistencies with scientific laws. For instance, much prominence has been given to the divergent theories on the nature of light. Certain phenomena suggest wave motion, others that light is propelled as bundles of energy. There is no present law which can bring together this apparent contradiction. Scientists, however, are confident that such a deeper law exists.

It can be seen from this that the scientist cannot and, in fact, does not any longer state that miracles are incredible just because he cannot fit them into his framework of things. Even in cases where miracles assume a set of events which are apparently contradictory to the best scientific knowledge, the scientist is still undaunted. In our day, he waits for the day when the apparent contradiction will be resolved.

This does not mean that we can return to the nineteenth century theological definition of miracle as the breaking or interruption of law. If miracle is to be included into the scheme of nature at all, it must be assumed that miracles, too, are governed by natural law. The fact that the processes of these laws which bring about the miracle are not known at this stage of knowledge does not mean that God did not use these channels. God is an orderly God, and He made an orderly universe. It would be very surprising if He used processes and means for everything else in the universe but left out miracles. This thinking means that the supernatural events in the world are merely natural events being used by God to bring about His purposes.

It seems obvious to many of us now that this idea of broken laws in miracles is untenable on theological grounds also. If God had to break His own laws to bring about miracles, then obviously they were not flexible enough for every purpose of God when He originally made them, which is another way of saying His original creation was imperfect. When God created the world, He saw that it was good. This also included the existence of natural law which must be flexible enough for every purpose which God has in mind. So we have to abandon the idea of miracles as broken laws.

This thought of God manipulating His own laws is very instructive. It means that miracles are exhibitions of God's knowledge rather than mere brute power or show of magic. It underlines the scientific truth that it is knowledge which is power. The way in which a scientist controls nature is by first gaining a knowledge of its laws, and then he can manipulate it for his purposes.

This can be seen especially in the conquest of certain diseases like malaria and yellow fever. Each of these diseases defied control until the medical scientists were able to understand the life cycle of the micro-organism which was the cause. Once they understood this, they were able to put a stop to its existence at stages in the life cycle when it was particularly vulnerable. This is also true of the modern conquest of polio. The same thing happened in physics. The great developments in nuclear energy are the direct results of the understanding of the law of nature that Einstein expressed as $E = mc^2$.

Because God is the Author of the universe, He obviously knows all its laws, and therefore it is easy for Him to manipulate these laws to bring about the desired results. Since His knowledge is so infinitely greater than ours, it is not surprising that His results are infinitely greater than ours, too. This also explains much of the miraculous in the life of Jesus. As the Son of God, He reflected the truth of God; therefore, miracle was inevitable. If there had been no outbreak of the supernatural, there would have been serious doubts about His divinity.

Once this principle is recognized, it is easy to fall into the temptation of trying to reconcile the miracles of the Christian religion in terms of modern science. This is a perilous procedure. What usually happens is that by the time the rather difficult reconciliation has been made, science itself has moved on and the theologian is left carrying the baby. In other words, the miracle is tied onto something no longer recognized to be true. The result is to bring fresh discredit upon the miracle.

Especially with the miracles of the Bible, it is obvious that we do not know with any confidence the circumstances that were existing at the time. And without a thorough knowledge of all the existing circumstances, it is impossible to trace the laws that God may have used.

A note of emphasis must be made here: Because in some cases advancing knowledge may explain a miracle, it does not mean that it has been explained away. For instance, in the book of Joshua it explains the method that God used to dry up the river Jordan so that the children of Israel could cross.[1] Apparently a land slide occurred up river and the water disappeared down the grade towards the Dead Sea, leaving the river temporarily dry. In this case, although we know the channels that God used, it does not lessen at all our confidence that God was the Author of it.

There was a time in the study of the supernatural when attempts were made to explain miracles as the imaginative interpretation of natural events by unsophisticated minds. This usually leads to greater difficulties than occur in the miracles themselves. For instance, in the story of Jesus walking on the water, it has been suggested that since it was dark, the disciples did not realize that Jesus was merely wading in ankle-deep water. It appeared to them that He was walking on it. When Peter jumped overboard, he really landed in this shallow water, and when he sank, he dropped into a hole. It seems reasonable enough until you begin asking how on earth the boat did not ground in ankle-deep water and how these experienced fishermen were not aware of the shallowness at this spot.

The Bible itself records the same kind of attempt by the Jews to explain the miracle of the Resurrection. They suggested that the soldiers claim that the disciples stole the body away while they were asleep. This makes it hard to explain how a whole cordon of soldiers on sentry duty would be asleep when they knew that this would most likely be followed by capital punishment. Or even if they were asleep, how could these rather cowardly disciples break through their lines, move the stone, and take Jesus away without even stirring the soldiers? Obviously, the explanation is more incredible than the miracle itself.

There also have been times when those who have been finding difficulty about the miracles of Christianity have been straining at a gnat and swallowing a camel. Most theologians have accepted readily enough the miracle of the Incarnation or the Resurrection, but they

[1]Joshua 3:16.

carp at lesser miracles like the feeding of the five thousand or the healing of the man that was born blind. Yet the idea of God becoming man and ultimately conquering the grave is intrinsically far more difficult.

It is the conviction of the author that much of the difficulty which we find in regard to the miraculous is due to our dulled and befogged sense of the presence of God. If we really believe in God and know that He is operating in our world, we should have no problem in expecting that tremendous things will occur which defy our explanation.

This does not mean that we should move into an area of gullible credulity with regard to miracles generally. It only means that we should keep an open mind until we know all the facts. With regard to the miracles of the Bible and of Christianity generally, a greater principle is operating. The Bible has been given to us by the inspiration of God, attested to by that Spirit throughout the centuries, and vindicated in its use by the same Spirit today. In view of this vindication by the Holy Spirit, we can accept the Scriptures as being reliable in every sense. Then with humble reliance on God and patient waiting for the development of further knowledge, we can wait until God ultimately shows how even the most difficult miracles of the Bible fit in nicely with the orderly scheme of the universe.

CHAPTER FOUR

The Mystery of Antiquity

As has been mentioned earlier, one of the first and most serious areas of conflict between religion and science has been in the matter of prehistory. How long has the universe, and particularly our earth, been in existence? How long has man himself been dwelling on this earth? Unfortunately, both the scientific and Biblical points of view are still veiled in mystery. Science seems to be no closer to decisive answers than it was one hundred and fifty years ago. Indeed, it appears to some of us that the question is much more confused now than when we were at school. As far as religion is concerned, a great deal depends on the interpretation of the Genesis accounts. There are a number of theories, but nothing definite enough to give us any assurance as to what a detailed Christian viewpoint can be.

It is universally agreed that the universe is of great antiquity, but the estimated age in billions of years is constantly being revised. It was assumed many years ago that the stellar system was formed first and that the solar system followed. There is no longer any certainty about this. The general opinion is that everything occurred by slow change; but then too, there are opinions that the universe might have come into being instantaneously.

Provided that we disregard the figurings of Archbishop Ussher mentioned earlier, we find the Biblical account is also inconclusive. It simply states that "In

40

the beginning God created the heavens and the earth" (Genesis 1:1). The second verse suggests that God made the present order of things out of an uninhabitable state, which possibly does suggest some form of development.

There was a time in the history of Christian thought when the so-called "catastrophe theory"[1] was popular. This claimed that God first made a perfect world but that it was destroyed during the Satanic rebellion. Creation was then repeated and built on the old ruins. The view is no longer seriously entertained.

During the last century, an ingenious theory was brought forward by a man named Edmund Gosse which deserves some consideration.[2] It was given scant attention then, but in view of modern ideas of the relativity of time, it is worth another hard look.

Gosse argued that although the acts of creation were instantaneous, they necessarily presupposed a prehistory that didn't really exist. Suppose that Adam was created the equivalent of a thirty-year-old man. He would have in his body all the earmarks of a previous thirty years which never occurred, for each body is the product of past physical change. For instance, he would have a navel, yet there could have been no umbilical cord.

The same would be true if a tree were created instantaneously. It would contain annular rings which could not correspond with any previous years. So on with all created things. When this reasoning is extended to the universe as a whole, you have a universe which must show a prehistory which did not actually occur. Geological history then is as necessary to universal creation as a residual body would be to the creation of a man in the height of his powers.

[1] A. Rendle Short, *Modern Discovery and the Bible* (Chicago: Inter-Varsity Press, 1955), pp. 96-98.
[2] Andrew Dickson White, *A History of the Warfare of Science With Theology* (New York: Appleton, 1922), I, 241-242.

The theory is analogous to the laws of reflection. Physics says that the apparent distance of the image of an object behind a mirror is the same as that of the object in front of it. Yet the image is an illusion. Look behind the mirror and there is nothing there.

The theory foundered on the objection that it was incredible that God should create a gigantic lie, even though intrinsically necessary for instantaneous creation. However, now that we have abandoned the absoluteness of time, the residual prehistory of instantaneous creation doesn't have to be an illusion. It could have really occurred, but in compressed time, in the lightning flash instant that preceded the finished work. That is, geologic history, the fossil record, the ravages of erosion, the radioactive rundown and all the other factors that would in our time reference take millions of years, in another time context could be momentary.

The view has the obvious advantage that it allows you to have your cake and eat it too. It is perfectly compatible with instantaneous creation (if that is assumed) and the geologic prehistory as well. However, it is far too soon to put much weight on it, because the conception of time is rather revolutionary, to say the least, at our present stage of knowledge.

This is obviously one of the areas in which we will have to wait for science to come to some more definitive position. At the moment, the figures suggested are projections of processes already occurring within the universe. This carries the assumption that these processes have always been the same. Although this is reasonable, it is by no means self-evident. Each attempt to measure time by radioactive rundown is based on assumptions involving freedom from contamination of rock samples and constancy of the very radioactive rundown in question. In any case, any conclusions about the age of the earth by scientists will simply fill the gaps in the account given in the Bible and cannot conceivably bring about any real conflict.

As far as the antiquity of man is concerned, the problem is more difficult, because the Bible does give more detail. The difficulties are twofold: those that come from paleontology and those that come from the theory of evolution.

Broadly speaking, paleontology is the study of fossilized forms in geological research. So far, skeletons that have been uncovered suggest that man may have been inhabiting this earth for at least 100,000 years. This can be an estimate only, and once again it is dependent upon estimates based upon the projection of present processes. Future research may bring about considerable revision.

For instance, at the time of writing there is considerable excitement about oxygen-18 research,[3] which gives an opportunity to determine temperatures on the earth in ancient times. Preliminary studies indicate that the ice age may have been far more recent than has been assumed. Since many estimates of human antiquity are based on ice age dating, this means that man's origin may have been far more recent than we have believed.

Once again it must be pointed out that the Genesis narrative does not suggest any date for the creation of man. We will obviously have to wait for further evidence to come in, but there is nothing here to give reason for great concern.

An interesting theory which has been propounded in recent years suggests that there may be a difference between "spiritual" and "natural" man.[4] That is, God could have created a being which was like man in physical form but was purely animal. This would account for the so-called "ape-man" and "men-apes" which are admitted now could not be modern man's ancestors anyway. If such a race of "natural" men existed, they became extinct like so many other species.

[3]Loren Eiseley, *The Immense Journey* (London: Thames & Hudson, 1957), p. 113.
[4]Short, *op. cit.*, pp. 114-115.

This would mean that Adam and Eve were the beginning of a new race altogether, which had the physical characteristics of the earlier being but were different in that they were made in the image of God. That is, they had spiritual and personality features which made them completely distinct. It has been suggested that the mention in Genesis 6:1, 2 of the "sons of God" and the "daughters of men" may refer to early conflicts between these two races.

The theory of evolution and its special difficulties will be dealt with in the next chapter. It is obvious that the decision on the adequacy of the evolution theory will have definite bearings on the antiquity of man. To put the problem into clear relief, we should consider here the possibility of what it would mean if the evolutionary origin of man were to be proved, even though at the moment this is far from being the case.

Under the evolutionary theory, we would have to assume that the Genesis narrative is referring to the climaxes of the physical evolution — in other words, when each species was complete. It would mean that God superimposed on two physically complete beings the spiritual and personality factors of uniqueness. In the language of the biologist, this could be considered as a mutation. This kind of thinking would consider the evolutionary processes as the means that God is using. The point being made here is that even if the origin of man on the evolutional hypothesis were proved to be correct, there still would be no insoluble difficulty for most Biblical interpreters. This is shown by the fact that there are even now a great many Christians who believe in evolution as now formulated and yet still have the deep conviction that the Bible is the inspired and authoritative Word of God.

Much of the controversy has arisen over the description of creation in terms of successive days in Genesis 1. One amazing thing here is that the order of creation is extremely close indeed to that which has been given by the geologists. For instance, André Senet in his *Man in Search of His Ancestors* writes: ". . . The Abbe de Lapparent, one of the greatest contemporary geologists said one day: 'If I had to summarize in a few lines the main events in the history of the earth I would copy out again the first paragraphs of Genesis.' "[5] To those who would deny the inspiration of the Biblical narrative, this presents a problem. How could a writer some three or four thousand years ago be able to think out the order of creation which has only been available to science itself in very recent years? You either have to say that the memory of the race at this stage was still remarkably clear on the creation events or else the information came from the Creator of the universe Himself.

The meaning of the term "day" used in Genesis 1 is wrapped in obscurity. Even the ancients wondered whether it was the "day of man" or the "day of God," referring to the statement in II Peter 3:8, "One day is with the Lord as a thousand years, and a thousand years as one day." But the general interpretation has been that this does refer to actual solar days. The reference to the evening and the morning in every case gives some credence to this.

In recent years, a great number of conservative theologians have felt that the day means an "age" or a long period of time — in fact, that the days of Genesis correspond to the long ages of geology. It is felt under this view that the discoveries of geology are helping us to interpret the Bible and giving us an understanding as to what the term "day" really means. However, it must be said that this view was more popular among conservative thinkers a generation ago than it is today.

Another view is that the days of Genesis are not days of creation, but days of revelation. It has been suggested that the Holy Spirit revealed the story of creation to the writer on successive days. Therefore,

[5]André Senet, *Man in Search of His Ancestors* (New York: McGraw-Hill Book Co. Inc., 1955), p. 264.

when he talks about what happened on a particular day, he does not mean that the events referred to happened in such a twenty-four hour period. The theory is ingenious but suffers again from the difficulty that this does not seem to be what the narrative is implying.

Another theory rather similar to this one is that the days of Genesis are merely a literary form used as a device to describe creation, as we would use chapters in a book. This suffers from the same difficulty as the previous theory.

It must be admitted that most Christians throughout the centuries, and today as well, when they read the story of creation come to the conclusion that God did create all things in six solar days. But the meaning of solar days at that time of antiquity is completely unknown to us. We cannot necessarily assume that the day then was our present twenty-four hours. The longevity of the patriarchs in Genesis also gives reason for thought in this connection. In his books,[6] Velikovsky shook the thinking of the scientists[7] who assume that the motion of heavenly bodies has always been the same as it is now. Sir James Jeans in his famous "tidal theory" thought that the planets were created by the temporary proximity of another star to our sun.[8] Incidents like this are clearly possible, and if they occurred they would leave little or no trace but would create a set of conditions very different from those we have now.

[6] Immanuel Velikovsky, *Worlds in Collision* (New York: The Macmillan Co., 1950), and *Ages in Chaos* (Garden City, New York: Doubleday and Co. Inc., 1952).

[7] This has been a shaking in anger rather than a shaking in convictions. His views have been almost universally rejected. But he has thrown into clear relief the fact that if the motion of heavenly bodies *were* different in ancient times, then quite a different scheme of physical events from what we experience now could have been operating on the earth.

[8] This was a version of the Chamberlain-Moulton Theory; see J. H. Rush, *The Dawn of Life* (Garden City, New York: Hanover House, 1957), pp. 51-53.

This does not mean that God could not have created our earth in six twenty-four hour days. This is His universe and He obviously can create it how and when He likes. It does not mean either that geologists and other thinkers who try to trace the footprints of God in the sands of time are necessarily right in their interpretations. Back in those ancient times, there could have been such an acceleration of physical processes that what would normally take millions of years could occur in twenty-four hours or less. Certainly the truth at the moment is that we do not know.

Perhaps the mystery of antiquity which is the most obscure of all is the origin of woman. Genesis 2:20-25 states that God caused a deep sleep to fall on Adam, took out one of his ribs, and from that rib created woman. The word for "rib" in Hebrew is exceedingly obscure and need not be translated that way at all. But in any case, it is obvious that the writer intends us to believe that woman was created out of part of the physical body of the first spiritual being.

This has seemed to many people to have all the marks of a myth or a legend. Yet it must be pointed out that Jesus apparently did not think this to be so. As God in human flesh, He accepted this as fact and based His "one flesh" doctrine of marriage upon it.[9] To conservative Christians this is decisive. Attempts to explain it figuratively founder on the rock that apparently this was not the viewpoint of Christ.

Notice that it is not claimed that this is the origin of female beings as such. There were obviously female animals long before this and maybe the female of "natural man," if such existed. This simply refers to female spiritual humans, "daughters of God," if you like. The concept is important because it forever pleads for the dignity of woman and the responsibility of man towards her.

But where does the real difficulty lie? It seems to the present author that our doubts about it are simply

[9]Matthew 19:4, 5.

due to our lack of awareness of God. An adequate, practical faith in Him as the Creator and the Ruler of the universe does not give us any problem, no matter what He chooses to do in this world, even if we cannot, in our ignorance, trace the methods that He uses.

In conclusion, it must be obvious that the interpretation of the Bible, as well as the scientific interpretation of nature, depends a great deal on the running of the time clock of the universe. Has it always run at uniform speed? Has it slowed or accelerated? What is time anyhow? Certainly the physics of relativity has made it impossible to think of time as an absolute. Here are mysteries which still defy penetration.

The answers may be far from what we imagine. In science, they usually are. Indeed, the scientific interpretation of nature is going farther and farther from what was expected. Objects are not solid, space is curved, we don't see what we think we do, gravity is not a force acting through a distance, and so on. This is what makes science so exciting, but also increasingly humbling.

But let us pause in the midst of all this mystery and realize that the Creator of all this profoundness was present in Christ. We can, therefore, rest with confidence in the Word of Christ that it tells us directly what scientists will also find out when their long search is successful.

CHAPTER FIVE

The Origin of Man

Of all the areas of dispute between religion and science, by far the most vicious controversies have arisen with regard to the origin of man and of living things. The main point of issue has been the theory of evolution as put forth by Charles Darwin in 1859. This claimed to give a naturalistic account of these origins, which not only seemed in many minds to do away with the necessity for divine origin but it also seemed contrary to the Biblical picture that the various kinds of living things, including man, were created separately.

Before going into details of this controversy, there are certain things which need to be said at the start which may pull out most of the teeth from the argument. First of all, the place of God as the Creator cannot be called into question for the simple reason that science cannot concern itself with ultimate origins. Scientists can examine processes, but cannot go beyond that. Whatever is the ultimate conclusion of scientists on the riddle of living things, all that can be done is to reveal how God carried out His work of creation. That is to say, scientists may explain how God works, but cannot explain away God.

For instance, if scientists should ultimately conclude that some form of evolutionary process is the explanation of the origin of all living things, then the most that could be deduced would be that God in His wisdom used such a process. The fact that evolution or any other theory cannot make God superfluous is amply illustrated by the fact that Charles Darwin himself in his book, *The Origin of Species,* says that in the beginning the Creator gave life to one of a few primary forms.[1] This, in his opinion, started everything off.

On the other hand, it is equally important for the student of the Bible to avoid reading into Scripture that which it does not say. It is easy to assume that when the Bible says that God created man from the dust of the earth, it means that He made some kind of mud and out of this formed a man in the same way that a kindergarten child forms an image of man out of clay. But the Bible does not say this. It gives no indication of the process that God used. If it should be found that this process was not instantaneous, this would not be surprising with a Creator who takes years to make an oak out of an acorn. He could make a mature man in a fraction of a second, but in fact He takes some twenty years and a very complicated and intricate process to do so. This does not mean that God could not have created the first man instantaneously. Indeed, He may well have done so, but it does mean that we cannot assume what the Bible does not in fact say.

Neither do the Bible texts often quoted against evolution give us a decisive answer. For instance, in Genesis 1 it constantly refers to each act of creation of living things to be "after his kind." But this gives no problem to the evolutionist because it refers to the finished act. So also with I Corinthians 15:39, which states, "All flesh is not the same flesh: but there is one kind of flesh of men, another flesh of beasts, another of fishes, and another of birds." That there are differences in the completed acts nobody denies. But this gives us no guidance on what happened before this.

[1]Charles Darwin, *The Origin of Species,* Chapter XV, last paragraph.

Apparently the answer to the riddle will ultimately have to come through science.

However, it should not be ignored that there is widespread distrust throughout the Christian world about the theory of evolution. Many of the arguments raised against it are invalid and the incidence of invective and hatred directed toward the evolutionists by some is to be deplored. But all this is evidence of a deep-down nagging feeling that something is wrong in this area of thought. Since the Holy Spirit works through believing Christians, He may be planting this concern. Human frailty is such that we cannot put too much weight on this assumption, but it should serve as a warning to act very carefully before assuming the evolutionary explanation is correct. It is no use objecting that the Christian world once thought the world was flat, for then Christians were merely reflecting current scientific opinion. Now Christians are uneasy even in spite of the fact that evolution in some form or other is generally assumed by the world of science, and this uneasiness remains after a hundred years.

It is often a matter of wonder to students of this subject that after a hundred years of research on biology, the theory of evolution is still a theory and not a law. It would appear at first sight that the matter ought by now to have been proved one way or another.

Of course you will often hear from some enthusiastic evolutionists that evolution is now indisputable, that it has been proved beyond doubt, and that anyone who disputes this is an ignoramus or a fanatic. This is jumping the gun to say the least. The vehemence of such statements makes one suspicious that the speakers are trying to convince themselves. When a scientific theory crystallizes into law, such as relativity, it speaks for itself. All we can say at the moment is that evolution is generally accepted, but with serious misgivings on the adequacy of some aspects of it. As for the kind of rigorous proof that scientists generally seek, it still isn't there. Indeed, some say that because of the philosophic aspects of the theory, that proof will never be possible.

There is a deep-seated reason for this uncertainty. The theory of evolution is partly science and partly philosophy. The part that is scientific is easy to verify and in most cases is beyond question. The other philosophic part is mostly in an area where proof one way or another is well nigh impossible. This philosophic part starts with the scientific facts and weaves a theory of their significance and relationship.

Dr. Lin Yutang in his book, *From Pagan to Christian,* after stating that he himself is a Darwinist, writes: "... the processes involved in the law of evolution, observed by a serious student and not superficially accepted, lead to and always end in metaphysics, that is in assumptions beyond the law of physics."[2]

Dr. Mortimer J. Adler of the University of Chicago, known for his Great Books work, rejects evolution entirely on its philosophic presuppositions. He calls it a "myth" and says he does so advisedly in order to refer to the elaborate conjectural history which vastly exceeds the evidence. He says it is the work of "philosophers."[3]

Now, of course, we cannot denounce a theory just because it is partly philosophic, but pointing out that there is a large philosophic element in the theory of evolution does put us on the alert for that subjectivity which is a necessary characteristic of philosophy. This is an entirely different realm from that of objective science. There is obviously room for many interpretations. Above all, there is a clear call for an open mind.

The theory of evolution states that all living things are related. At the beginning there was one living cell and out of this developments have occurred with ever increasing variations until we have the world of nature

[2]Lin Yutang, *From Pagan to Christian* (Cleveland: World Publishing Co., 1959), p. 217.
[3]Mortimer J. Adler, *What Man Has Made of Man* (New York: Frederick Unger Publishing Company, 1937), pp. 115 ff.

as we see it now. The developments and variations have been said to be due to the law of natural selection. This seems to mean that in the struggle for survival the characteristics which are useful for survival persist and creatures with those elements which are not so useful or which are otherwise handicapped die out. It is further said that this whole process is governed by chance.

Man is considered to be a product, possibly the final product, of this system. As to what his ancestry has been, there is no unanimity of opinion. The popular idea is that his descent is from the higher anthropoid apes or else that man and the ape have a common ancestor. The critical point of issue is the assumption of this theory that man was not separately created but is himself a by-product of animal life.

Curiously enough, it does not seem that having a theory to explain the relation between living things is as essential from a practical point of view as was once thought. As a matter of fact, there are colleges and schools now which are perfectly able to teach biology without any omissions or problems at all and without even mentioning the theory of evolution. In fact, some of them are prevented from doing so by law and others by religious principles. And yet if you were to take a good student from one of these schools and compare his knowledge with one of those of equal ability from a school where evolution is taught, you would find that there would be no significant difference in their biological information at all.

A good illustration of this is the brilliance of Seventh Day Adventist doctors. Although medicine is directly dependent on biology, and evolution is completely absent from their thinking on biology, yet nevertheless they are some of the finest doctors in the world.

Perhaps it will be worthwhile to look at the main evidences for the theory of evolution and see those strange bedfellows, science and philosophy, at work together.

The most telling point for the theory is the sameness that basically exists in all living things. By careful arrangements, you can construct a tree of descent starting from one single cell in increasing complexity to man himself. Each creature in this succession has features in common with those below it but also individual peculiarities as well. So far, this is indisputable science. Now philosophy comes in. It says that each unit developed into the next by a series of infinitesimal gradations. It is something like a moving picture. It is composed of a series of individual still pictures but the eye interprets as one moving image. Notice, though, how the interpretation of science goes beyond the facts themselves.

Actually, you can make two guesses. The evolutionary one would be that the Creator started that first cell evolving and continued it in one vast process of creation. Of course, then you would have to explain the gaps in the present record of living things. Why is it not a continuum now? In answer, you could probably say that it would be if many creatures had not become extinct. The other guess is that the good Lord made His first living thing so perfectly that He decided to make all the rest in the same pattern, including such modifications as would suit His purpose for each. That way, you would not have any gaps to explain. Of course this would mean multitudinous separate acts of creation. But would this bother God any more than one act? And even Darwin admitted that there would have to be one act of creation to start things off.[4]

Which guess is right? At this stage of knowledge, nobody knows. But notice that the philosophy of the so-called and often despised "fundamentalist" is, if anything, simpler than that of the evolutionist.

Seemingly corroborative to the evidence from comparative anatomy, as described in the previous paragraphs, is the fossil record. If there is a continuum of living things, the remains in the geological strata of

[4]*Loc. cit.*

the ages should show this. Generally speaking, the record may be interpreted as progressive gradation from primitive living things in the earlier strata to more complex in the later.

The guess that the gaps in the continuum of comparative anatomy are due to forms having become extinct, is partly borne out by fossil evidence of the previous existence of such forms. However, there are still huge gaps in the continuum with no explanation whatever except that of the imperfection of the geological record.

Although the fossil record is generally one of progression, this is not so in every case. Sometimes you find more complex forms preceding the simpler forms. In some instances, this may have been due to inversion of strata by by-gone geological catastrophes. However, there are many instances which cannot be explained this way. A clear case in point is that of the South African Boskopoids[5] which, although supposedly alive ten thousand years ago, nevertheless show characteristics which under evolutionary reasoning could not be expected for many years hence and are superior to modern man.

Great care needs to be exercised in interpreting the fossil record. The study has been plagued with fraud and forgery. This apparently has been true since earliest times, but was brought into public notice in 1953 when it was announced that the famous bones of the so-called Piltdown Man were a hoax.[6] The disturbing feature here is that this could go undiscovered by paleontologists for forty years. This is no fault of these scientists, but it does show how uncertain and subjective this kind of study is. Actually, all we have to go on in any particular case are a few bones and perhaps a few artifacts. Then it is also difficult to tell at times whether the characters are really new forms

[5]Loren Eiseley, *The Immense Journey* (London: Thames & Hudson, 1957), pp. 123-140.
[6]J. S. Weiner, *The Piltdown Forgery* (London: Oxford University Press, 1955).

rather than diseased normal forms. Obviously, the amount of guesswork involved in interpreting what the creatures were like is enormous. For this reason, the reconstructions by artists that you see in popular magazines and even in museums should be disregarded.

As far as any immediate ancestry of modern man is concerned, apparently, the fossil record has nothing to offer. Until the concept of man as a "made-over" ape was abandoned,[7] such superapes as "Java Man," "Pekin Man," "Neanderthal Man," etc., could be brought forward, but now that evolutionists think that modern man is not in that line of descent, this is no longer possible. On present evidence, man as we know him, appears in the fossil record pretty well as we see him now.

To sum up the evidence from the fossils, then, the idea of an evolutional continuum is given some support by the filling in of some of the gaps but is weakened somewhat by the presence of inversions with the process reversed. The theory of special creations remains relatively untouched either way, except that the lack of any record of immediate ancestors for man tends to support it.

Some attention has been given to the phenomena of what is known as "vestigial remains" as pointers to an evolutionary ancestry. This simply means that there are in the bodies of some living things organs which no longer appear to be useful and which would have been useful in a previous stage of development — for instance, the vermiform appendix in human beings. This leans very heavily upon the assumption that just because we cannot find any usefulness for the particular organ now, therefore it cannot be useful — a not very humble attitude at our stage of knowledge.

In any case, occurrences of these vestigial remains are so rare that one can put little evidential value upon them.

[7]André Senet, *Man in Search of His Ancestors* (New York: McGraw-Hill Book Co. Inc., 1955), p. 59.

As a matter of fact, the argument is somewhat two-edged for the following reason: If all living things are part of an original continuum, then any one creature is a vertical cross-section. A glance at that cross-section should show many evidences of the continuum below it. In other words, there should be a great many of these remnants. In the case of man, there should be many vestigial remains which have not had time to die out. Their absence is suspicious to say the least.

Recent works on evolution have given only scant treatment to the theory of vestigial remains. Apparently, it is not regarded any longer as being of serious evidential value.

This is also true of the famous embryological or recapitulation argument, which states that the embryo of a living creature repeats the whole process of evolution up to that stage. The so-called "gill slits" in the human foetus, for instance, were explained as evidence of fish ancestry. However, Dr. A. Rendle Short, who spent a lifetime in the study of anatomy, states that this identification is an error.[8] The features referred to are not gill slits but grooves between arches that support blood vessels. Dr. Short notes that Julian Huxley in his book defending evolution, *Evolution, the Modern Synthesis,* ignores the recapitulation argument.[9]

The reason why nineteenth century scientists put such emphasis on the recapitulation theory was because it was a logical theoretical deduction from the theory of evolution. If evolution is correct, this is what ought to occur. The abandonment of recapitulation is therefore negative evidence against the theory of evolution itself.

It has been noted that in some isolated areas, such as islands, some of the forms do seem to group themselves into families, the members of which may not be found anywhere else. This is fairly definite evi-

---

[8]A. Rendle Short, *Modern Discovery and the Bible* (Chicago: Inter-Varsity Press, 1955), p. 106.
[9]*Ibid.,* p. 76.

dence of relationship. As a matter of fact, this type of limited relationship is beyond dispute anyway. The point in question is not whether there are certain families of living things which are related but whether the whole of creation is related. In the case of island forms, these bridges which do exist only occur between creatures which are very similar indeed.

A great deal of attention has been given to domestic botany and zoology. Work like that of Luther Burbank[10] in California makes it obvious that it is possible to breed new forms differing from parent forms. But once again this type of breeding is very limited. Where it is possible to create hybrids, most cases of these are infertile. That is, the evidence from this area shows that some interrelationship does exist, but it does not go very far.

This variety, change, and modification within groups of living things is a scientific fact. Where the philosophy begins is when the jump is made beyond this evidence to say that this is evolution in action by assuming this spread is unlimited and shows how one species develops into another. Even in lands like Australia which has been isolated from the rest of the world for ages, this kind of modification shows no widespread extension. The best human ingenuity can produce new varieties of snapdragons out of the parent plant and better race horses from the original stock and can even succeed in a certain amount of cross-breeding, but apparently cannot exceed certain limits.

One problem that worried Darwin a great deal was the lack of geologic time to fit in the millions of years required for the theory of evolution.[11] This difficulty still remains. For instance, a great deal of thought has been given to the natural history of the horse. It has been claimed that it is possible to trace

[10]Henry Smith Williams, *Luther Burbank* (London: Grant Richards Ltd., 1915).
[11]Loren Eiseley, *Darwin's Century* (Garden City, New York: Doubleday and Co. Inc., 1958), p. 235.

modifications from the tiniest form to the most complex form, but that this took a vast period of time — possibly one hundred million years, maybe more. According to recent estimates, living things have been on the earth for one and a half billion years. Thus the changes of the horse alone takes up a significant fraction of evolutionary time. Yet the span that would be required for this is only small in comparison with the supposed total process of evolution. Granted many of these modifications could be carried on simultaneously, but it still seems rather difficult to crowd in all this within the limitations of geologic time as commonly accepted today.

Half a century ago when deVries came out with his theory of mutations,[12] it looked as if he might have found an explanation for the embarrassing gaps in the evolutionary continuum. According to this theory new forms proceed out of previous forms not by gradations but in sudden jumps and fully formed. This amounts to something like special or separate creations but on naturalistic terms. However, the mutation theory cannot be used to support the evolutionary philosophy very well[13] because no means are available to explain the origin of *new* genes. Mutations, as studied almost endlessly in fruit flies *(Drosophila)*, are known as changes in genes that influence already existing physical traits. We observe new and different characteristics but not new traits. Therefore the mutation theory does not help scientists explain how new physical traits could come into existence. But appearance of new physical traits is required for any change of one animal kind into another animal kind (or one plant kind into another plant kind), which is supposedly involved in evolution.

Much weaker than the theory of an evolutionary continuum is the suggested process of natural selection which is thought to have been the mechanics of evolu-

[12]G. S. Carter, *A Hundred Years of Evolution* (New York: The Macmillan Co., 1957), p. 104.
[13]Darwin, *op. cit.*, Chapter VII.

tion. As has been said earlier, natural selection means that living forms are perpetuated which happen to develop characteristics which give them an advantage in the struggle for survival.

Now any treatment on scientific logic will emphasize that a hypothesis cannot be considered proved unless it covers all known facts and has no facts contrary to it. These criteria cannot be met by natural selection.

Nature is crowded with features which cannot be explained in terms of usefulness in the survival struggle. A historic case in point is that of the human brain, which gave so much trouble to Wallace,[14] Darwin's colleague in evolution. It goes far beyond that which would be required for survival. Natural selection cannot, without torturous laboring, give any explanation for such things as beauty, culture, music, and these other luxuries of living.

Then also, handicapping features have a habit of surviving, especially in man. His naked body and his long, helpless infancy made him a sitting duck for extinction, yet these features nevertheless developed. The timid and vulnerable sheep has survived, but ferocious reptiles have died out.

The case against natural selection is put very definitely by Robson and Richards in *The Variation of Animals in Nature:* "There is so little positive evidence in its favor, so much that appears to tell against it ... that we have no right to assign to it the main causative role in evolution."[15]

One particular aspect about natural selection that rather shocks those trained in the physical sciences is the tremendous odds against some of these variations occurring. The physicist would put little credence upon a hypothesis with a probability of being true of less than one in one hundred. Yet here the odds are fantastic. For instance, Dr. Lin Yutang says in his book that

[14]Eiseley, *op. cit.,* pp. 303 ff.
[15]G. C. Robson and O. W. Richards, *The Variation of Animals in Nature,* as in Short, *op. cit.,* p. 68.

the probability of the rattlesnake's poison apparatus occurring by chance variation is 1 in 10^{23}, that is, only once in one hundred thousand billion billion![16] Yet according to natural selection, the world is full of such occurrences.

Dr. Lin Yutang refers to the fact that sometimes some amazing odds do turn up at a gambling casino, yet if you have several of these at one time, you soon assume the game is crooked.[17] That is, it is not chance operating but design. (Incidentally, Dr. Lin Yutang does not object to evolution as such but only to its materialistic philosophy).

On this point, Rendle Short quotes Sir Arthur Keith, the noted British biologist, as saying that to state that the evolution of man has been determined by a series of chance events is biologically unbelievable.[18]

In the early days of the theory of evolution, a great deal was said about mimicry. As an illustration of natural selection, some living creatures have harmless characteristics which strongly resemble deadly features in other creatures and which therefore serve as a protective device by misleading potential enemies. For instance, if a snake which is harmless were to develop characteristics which could be mistaken for a rattlesnake, then this would prevent other creatures from attacking it and would therefore be a factor in its survival. Mimicry includes also such things as imitative coloring, habits, movements, sounds, pose, and environment. The suggestion under the natural selection hypothesis that these are chance variations which survived because they were useful seems rather far-fetched. Each of these features, under evolutionary reasoning, would be the end of a long process. During the process, the feature would be useless. Therefore how did it come to persist? The idea of design behind it all seems to be much more reasonable here.

[16]*Op. cit.*, p. 216.
[17]*Ibid.*, pp. 213, 214.
[18]*Op. cit.*, p. 70.

A similar idea in evolution — sexual selection — has been abandoned. It was said that the reason why some creatures have gay colors was to be able to attract the opposite sex for mating purposes. The fatal blow to this theory is the realization that many of these creatures do not have the retina capacity to be able to distinguish these colors anyway!

If natural selection is not adequate to explain the development of species, then what is? At the moment, there is no answer on naturalistic terms.

A great deal of damage has been done by well meaning people who tend to suppress the theory of evolution in view of its possible dangers to the Christian religion. The Christian religion has nothing to be afraid of. Let scientists examine where they will. The answer will ultimately vindicate the Word of God.

One instance of this well meaning but unwise type of protection was the Scopes trial in 1925.[19] This young man was tried by the state of Tennessee for daring to teach the theory of evolution. He was opposed by none other than William Jennings Bryan. After a sensational trial, he was found guilty and fined a hundred dollars, but this was later rescinded. However, through it all the Word of God was badly manhandled and Christianity came under a great deal of disrepute. This kind of method must always lead to disaster.

It is also hoped that as the years go on, conservative theologians will stand firm and wait calmly for God to reveal His own truth to persons seeking understanding about questions of origins. The Bible believer may very well use his God-given abilities graciously to show that the Bible provides the only unchanging answers about origins of the universe, the earth, life, man, and man's culture. Further he can show clearly and firmly that evolution is still only a theory because so many speculative and uncheckable ideas are involved.

[19]Sheldon N. Grebstein, Editor, *Monkey Trial* (The State of Tennessee vs. John Thomas Scopes) (Boston: Houghton Mifflin Company, 1960).

CHAPTER SIX

Special Difficulties in the Bible

The purpose of this chapter is to investigate some of the areas of the Bible which have come under special criticism, usually because they report events which seem, at least at first sight, to be contrary to our normal experience or known scientific laws.

Many of these incidents are miracles and therefore come under the considerations already given in chapter three on the subject of the supernatural, but some added discussion here may be helpful.

It must be kept in mind right from the start that we are not attempting to prove the Bible. As has been emphasized earlier, we accept the Bible, not because it is reasonable or agrees with science but because it has the authority of Christ. In other words, we would on this basis still accept the Scriptures even if they were unreasonable or unscientific. All we want to do is examine the problems in the light of the best scientific knowledge at our disposal.

Neither are we going to engage in torturous explanations to try and drag out a harmony between the Biblical incident under discussion and the relevant facts of science. Such explanations are often more difficult to believe than the Bible miracle. If an explanation doesn't easily fit, it should not be forced; and even if it does fit, it still may not be the correct explanation.

The main areas of possible error in any explanations are as follows: our interpretations of the incident, our appraisal of the relevant scientific facts, our ignorance of the details of the incident, and our ignorance of prevailing conditions at the time.

It is very important to realize that our knowledge of the details of the Biblical miracles is very limited indeed. Attempts to explain something when our knowledge of the facts is inadequate almost always lead to error. Therefore, the student of Biblical science should proceed very humbly, knowing that he is investigating areas of great mystery in which God Himself has been working.

We should keep in mind that we are on rather shaky ground when we assume that the operation of natural phenomena is exactly the same now as it was then. Our earth is scarred with the marks of ancient disasters of which we know very little. We know that there have been major climatic and geographic differences. There may have been other drastically changed conditions, too. A few years ago, Immanuel Velikovsky[1] caused quite a sensation when he published his theory that in Old Testament times the solar system was subjected to awful disturbances because of planetary collisions and near collisions. He suggested that Venus, which he says the ancient authorities refer to as a comet, collided with the earth and lost its tail. He also concluded that Mars once came to such proximity to the earth that the earth's motion was very erratic for a long time. Velikovsky's theories have not received any scientific support but are nevertheless of interest to the Biblical scholar because if the conditions he refers to did come about, then many Old Testament events would take on an entirely different outlook. The fact is that we know so little about the ancient world that we cannot make any assumptions about what did or did not occur. Yet we would need this to give an adequate explanation of what happened in any particular event.

[1] Immanuel Velikovsky, *Worlds in Collision* (New York: The Macmillan Co., 1950).

It is also noteworthy that Charles Darwin suggested that the process of change in the biological world may have been much faster at one stage of the universe than it is now.[2] Once again, it must be readily admitted that most scientists do not concur with Darwin on this. But when it is seriously suggested by a scientist of his eminence, it is evidence that we cannot assume that things existing today are the same as they have always been. To judge or explain a Biblical miracle of ancient times by the operation of laws now operating is a perilous proceeding indeed.

Since the previous chapters have already dealt with the difficulties of the creation story, there is no need for further discussion here. However, there are a couple of other matters about the antediluvian period which do need to be mentioned.

The first is the question of Cain's wife (Genesis 4:17). She could have been his sister. At one stage of knowledge, this would entail a weakened human race because of inbreeding. However, it is now known that this does not necessarily follow. For instance, the royal house of Fiji has been in-breeding for centuries, yet they represent some of the finest specimens on the island. The question of prohibited degrees of blood relationship would not have been in effect at this stage of the human race.

She could have been a member of some other near-human creation. Some attention has been given to this theory in a previous chapter. Others have suggested that Adam and Eve were not the only people created, because the Bible says, "Male and female created he *them*" (Genesis 1:27), the last pronoun possibly implying more than one couple. This is possible, but not a necessary inference. If it were true, it would mean that the Bible is only concerned with Adam's line. The others would have been extinguished at the Flood anyhow.

[2] Charles Darwin, *The Origin of Species* (New York: Modern Library), p. 253.

Another problem in the pre-flood days is the longevity of the people, extending in one case to over 900 years (Genesis 5:27). There are two possible explanations for this that are immediately evident.

The first is that their concept of a year was radically different from ours. That there was some confusion on this point is seen from the ancient records other than the Bible which also emphasized this longevity. A list of ancient Babylonian kings gives spans of life extending in some cases to 1200 years.[3] The Berossos list[4] of antediluvian kings indicates length of reign for a single person to be 100 times as much, extending in one case to 64,800 years! Apparently their year unit was not only different from ours but also varied among themselves. If we could find out exactly what the Genesis antediluvian year was, the problem would be simplified enormously.

Another point of view is that it isn't their longevity which was abnormal but our brevity! In those early days, sin would not have brought about the ravages that came later. The human body is built and designed for much longer life than we enjoy. It becomes prematurely aged by adverse conditions that God never intended. There is a lot of truth in this.

When we come to Noah's Flood, we move into a series of events which present real difficulties and yet have a surprising amount of attesting evidence. There is no doubt that Noah's Flood or some similar inundations in the ancient world is part of the memory of many races, because there are quite a number of references to such an event in the ancient literature of peoples spread all over the globe.

One particular cuneiform tablet from Nineveh, dated seventh century B.C., is particularly interesting. It is usually called "The Gilgamesh Epic."[5] In it the

[3]George A. Barton, *Archaeology and the Bible* (Philadelphia: American Sunday School Union, 1937), Chapter V.
[4]*Loc. cit.*
[5]*Ibid.,* Chapter VI.

gods gave command to build a ship in which the seed of life of all kinds was to be preserved. It was to be 120 cubits square and covered with bitumen. The man and his family entered the ship with the other living things. A fearful deluge overpowered everything and covered the mountains. When the flood had abated, a dove was sent out as a test but it returned because it could find no resting place. Finally, a raven was sent for the same purpose and did not return.

There can be no doubt that Noah's Flood is being referred to here. In the other accounts, the resemblances are not so clear but the general drift is unmistakable. Yet careful study shows that there is no literary dependence of these accounts on the Bible or vice versa. Apparently, knowledge of Noah's Flood in ancient times was well-known.

There is also some archaeological evidence to substantiate the account of the Flood. It is true that the deposits which have been found cannot be proved beyond doubt to be the results of *Noah's* Flood, but they do show that a flood of this proportion did occur in ancient times. As a matter of fact, in some minds it appears that the flood in the geological record may have been of greater proportions than Noah's Flood.

The first of these discoveries was in 1929 near Ur of the Chaldees when Sir Leonard Woolley found a layer eight feet deep of water-laid clay.[6] A similar discovery was made at Kish by Dr. Stephen Langdon. Langdon's appraisal of the significance is particularly clear.

He said: "When we made these observations . . . we were loath to believe that we had confirmation of the Deluge of Genesis, but there is no doubt about it now."[7]

[6]Sir Leonard Woolley, in an article in *The London Times* (March 15, 1929), as in A. Rendle Short, *Modern Discovery and the Bible* (Chicago: Inter-Varsity Press, 1955), p. 134.
[7]Sir Leonard Woolley, in an article in *The London Times* (March 18, 1929), as in A. Rendle Short, *op. cit.*

In spite of statements and findings like this, the cautious Biblical student will still stop short of saying that the account of Noah's Flood has been vindicated by archaeological discovery. It would be safer to say that archaeological discovery has shown that the occurrence of a flood of these proportions is feasible.

The physical causes of the Flood are not known to us, but it seems to be very evident that it was not caused merely by constant rain, as many people believe. The Bible itself refers to the "fountains of the great deep" being broken up (Genesis 7:11). This suggests some subterranean upheaval which sometimes occurs with earthquakes or volcanic eruptions. The bed of the Mediterranean or Caspian or Persian Gulf could have been raised, causing the water to flow over the surrounding terrain. Velikovsky suggested that the temporary proximity of a heavenly body to this earth at that time caused gigantic tides which swept around the earth and caused the deluge.[8] This, however, would mean that the Flood was not continuous but a succession of deluges, for while the tide was racing around one side of the world, the other would be normal.

Some discussion has gone on as to whether the Flood was a local flood or whether over the whole complete earth. The reason for the discussion is that the word used translated "earth" in Genesis 7:4 also means "land." Therefore, an equally good translation would make it appear that the whole land or area of Mesopotamia was inundated rather than the whole earth as we know it now. Against this, though, is the fact that there are memories of the Flood all over the world. Of course, some of these could have come through hearsay. Again, we do not know.

Many have questioned the account of the preservation of life in Noah's Ark, pointing out the difficulties that God would encounter in bringing creatures from all over the world to Noah or taking them back again after the Flood was over. This objection assumes

[8]*Op. cit.*, pp. 70 ff.

that the Flood was worldwide, which may not have
been the case, as we have seen. But in any case, saying
what God can or cannot do because of the difficulties
that we would encounter if we were in God's place is
impertinent thinking, to say the very least of it. Once
our thinking is based upon the Biblical demand that
God was in and behind all this, we cannot be any longer surprised at anything that could happen.

The story of the tower of Babel in Genesis 11
tells of the fantastic attempt of these ancient people in
their pride to reach up to God Himself and how God
used their very action to confound them. It is suggested
that this accounts for differences in language.

Curiously enough, there is evidence that the
remains of this Tower of Babel, as it is called, were
extant until comparatively recent times.[9] Heroditus
gives a description of it,[10] and there can be little doubt
that it refers to the same structure.

It is interesting to note that there is an ancient
fragment[11] which tells of the gods being offended at
the building of a certain structure. It says the gods
broke it down, scattered them abroad, and "made
strange their speech." The likeness to the Genesis
account is remarkable.

The incident in the Bible maintains that originally
there was one language which later became diversified.
This seems to be borne out by the study of languages
throughout the world. There are words and other features common to them all, suggesting that originally
they had a common ancestor.

The account of the destruction of Sodom and
Gomorrah (Genesis 19) refers to a terrible disaster in
ancient times. Suggestions have been given from time
to time that the cities referred to are now under the
Dead Sea, but perhaps more likely they were com-

[9]Cunningham Geikie, *Hours With the Bible* (New York: James
Pott & Co., 1905), I, 217 ff.
[10]*Ibid.*, p. 219.
[11]Joseph P. Free, *Archaeology and Bible History* (Wheaton,
Illinois: Scripture Press, 1950), p. 46.

pletely destroyed by the very nature of the disaster. The presence of rock salt, sulphur, asphalt, oil, and other minerals in the neighborhood shows that the raw materials were there for such an event. There is evidence that while this area was inhabited around about the time of Abraham, it was not again under civilized influence until Roman times. This is what you would expect on the basis of the Biblical account.

It should be mentioned here that the turning of Lot's wife into a pillar of salt (Genesis 19:26) is not a reference to a metamorphosis. The original merely means she became embedded in a block of salt when it landed on her during the explosion.

The account of the plagues in Egypt (Exodus 7-12) presents a number of problems. The plagues were as follows: blood, frogs, lice, flies, murrain, boils, hail, locusts, darkness, and death of the firstborn. Most of these plagues have had parallels many times since. For instance, the author has seen a plague of locusts so intense that a city of 350,000 was paralyzed.

The turning of the Nile waters into putrefying blood is unique, or at least seems that way, maybe because we do not have the details. Some have suggested that the word for "blood" could refer to some algae-like infestation.

Hail accompanied by fire is not surprising because hail is usually the product of electrical storms. This could also have been a meteoric shower, for the Hebrew word translated "hail" does not necessarily mean that.

The darkness "that could be felt" sounds like a sandstorm. The death of firstborn could have been caused by a number of diseases.

However, even if we were sure of every process involved, the occurrence, the discontinuance, and selectivity of the plagues could not be naturalistically explained. Here is a very direct manipulating of the processes of nature.

As far as the crossing of the Red Sea (Exodus 14) is concerned, the Bible gives its own explanation of the process used. It says that the waters were caused to recede by a strong east wind (Exodus 14:21). This kind of thing has been noted at other times. For instance, it is reputed that once the waters of the Lake Menzaleh were driven back seven miles. However, the fact that this event was controlled to fit a clear-cut time schedule shows that this could not have been a mere accidental, natural event.

With regard to the crossing of the River Jordan, we are on firmer ground. The Bible itself suggests (Joshua 3:16) that the river was dammed up in the neighborhood of the city of Adam. The water would then flow down the gradient towards the Dead Sea leaving the river dry until the landslide dam was broken again. This has occurred a number of times in history. But once again the timing points to supernatural control.

Perhaps the strangest of all the Old Testament miracles is the story of Joshua's long day. The reference (Joshua 10:13) states that the sun and moon "stood still in the midst of heaven, and hasted not to go down about a whole day." As has been mentioned elsewhere, we need not cavil at the language that is used. There is no evidence here that the Bible is insisting that the sun is in motion rather than the earth. It is an idiom which we ourselves use when we say that the sun rises and sets, without meaning to impugn what we know about our sun-centered universe.

Sir Ambrose Fleming's suggestion that God may have caused a temporary change in the refractive index of the atmosphere is well-known.[12] Under normal conditions, we see the sun for a few minutes after it has actually sunk below the horizon. This instance of refraction causes us to see an apparent image of the sun where in fact the sun is not. The amount of this

[12]Ambrose Fleming, *Proceedings of the Physical Society* (London: 1914), p. 318.

kind of distortion depends upon the gases in question. For instance, Rendle Short points out that if the atmosphere were composed of krypton, we would be able to see the sun wherever it was.[13] The attraction of this kind of explanation is that it does not involve any disturbance of the earth's rotation.

Velikovsky made some calculations as to what would be the effects of the proximity of Mars, which he believed to be the cause at that time. He concluded that on this hypothesis the derangements mentioned by Joshua are perfectly feasible.[14] However, the catch is that his hypothesis is far from being substantiated.

These suggestions are interesting, but it is impossible to evaluate them because the record of Joshua's long day tells us only that daylight was prolonged and that the apparent motion of the sun ceased for many hours. This must have been the end result of a whole complex of conditions the nature of which we cannot even guess at because we have no idea what they were. It has often been objected that if the earth were suddenly to cease rotation, the effects would be disastrous. This would be true unless a set of opposing conditions were set up to counter this effect.

It is certain that if God had stopped the earth's rotation in this case, He certainly would have provided for the after-effects. There would have been no point in God providing this miracle to help Joshua and then as a result have them all fly off at a tangent into space! In any case, the Bible does not say that God stopped the earth's rotation. It is interesting to note that ancient people have left on record references to a long day in the past.

There was another outbreak of miracles in the days of Elisha and Elijah. In these cases, the information is particularly meager.

[13]A. Rendle Short, *Modern Discovery and the Bible* (Chicago: Inter-Varsity Press, 1955), p. 157.
[14]*Op. cit.*, pp. 39 ff.

In II Kings 4 there is a record of how Elisha instructed a needy woman to continue to fill empty vessels from the only full one she had. Through this miraculous increase, she was able to pay her debts and save her sons from slavery. There are a number of cases in the Bible of accelerated multiplication of living things, but usually these cases were still associated with the source of life like the plagues of Egypt where the connection is reproduction. However, in this case, as in the incident of Christ's feeding of the five thousand, the material which is multiplied is isolated from its original life source. Consequently, we haven't a clue as to the processes used. As to possible analogies, one could cite the multiplication of substance, as in dough into bread, rice when boiled, the making of some synthetic substances, although this does not fall into any of these categories. But God knows far more about physical and chemical change than we do.

In II Kings 5, Naaman the Syrian is cured of leprosy while obeying a divine command to bathe in Jordan. However, there is no suggestion that the water was the curative element. Apparently, it was simply a test of his willingness to obey God. Since "leprosy" in ancient times covered a host of skin diseases, we cannot define this as Hansen's Bacillus, or modern leprosy. Once again there is no indication as to what process was used.

One of the more unusual miracles was that of the ax which, after falling into the stream, floated at the word of the prophet (II Kings 6:6). The conditions which could bring this about are open to a great deal of conjecture. We do not even know what the axhead was made of. Whether it would float in a liquid would depend upon its composition and that of the liquid and also on its motion. A fast running stream may easily bring a heavy boulder to the surface. The presence of unusual chemicals or minerals in the water might also give the ax a buoyancy which it would not have otherwise had. Here the prophet used a stick to locate the ax, but it does not explain exactly what happened. In the absence of the facts, we can only guess.

The story of Jonah has been the butt of jokes and cynicisms for years. Perhaps the most vigorous silencer that could be given against the criticism that the event was impossible is that a parallel has actually occurred. In 1931 a man on a whaling expedition fell into the water after his boat had been smashed by the tail of a whale. The next thing he knew, he was sliding down a dark passage. Realizing that he was inside the whale, his terror mounted so that he became unconscious. Two days later, as the whale was being cut up after capture, the body of the man was found in its stomach. After some slight medical attention, he was brought to consciousness and normal health. His skin had suffered somewhat from the acids in the whale's stomach, but apart from that he was completely unhurt.

Some suggestions have been made that the whale's mouth and throat are too small to accommodate a man. Of course, the scripture does not specify in the original language that it was a whale. Any great fish would do. But there is a species of whale which is capable of swallowing a man without any difficulty.[15] This animal also has the curious feature about it that on approaching death, it vomits up the contents of its stomach on the nearest shore. This could have been what happened to Jonah.

It is noteworthy here that Jesus referred to this story as an actual event (Matthew 12:40). If He, as the Son of God, found no particular difficulties about it, should we then, when our wisdom is infinitely less than His? To say the least, an incident like this is very unusual, but any direct action of God on this earth is bound to be unusual.

When we come to the life of Jesus upon earth, we can expect an outbreak of the supernatural since He was the manifestation of God in human flesh. Since all

15"Whale," *The World Book Encyclopedia* (1950 Edition), XVIII, 8728.

things were made by Him (John 1:3), it would have been very surprising indeed if there had not been evidences of the Great Architect at work in His creation.

The account of the virgin birth (Matthew 1:18-25; Luke 1:26-38) has troubled many, mainly because pregnancies in our experience occur only through male action. Some studies in recent years on "parthenogenesis"[16] have shown that we should not be so sure about this, especially in some of the lower animal forms. In any case, the giving of life in the normal manner of penetration of an ovum by a spermatozoon is still a mystery known only to God. The greatest miracle of all is life itself. Surely it should not be felt incredible that the God who can accomplish that great feat should vary His manner of bringing it about when His purposes demand it!

Our Lord's miracles of healing show unmistakable evidences of His divine knowledge. As we study them, we find in some cases instances of the use of psychophysical principles only discovered by us in recent years. A fair summary of human illness would be to say that it is caused by physical malfunction or the invasion of organisms. Modern medicine and surgery in both of these areas has become possible by our increasing knowledge of the human body and its functions, and of the life history of these organisms. Christ had perfect knowledge of all this which we know so imperfectly, apparently so much so that He could employ methods which need no obvious physical processes at all.

The instances of the resurrection from the dead can be explained in the same terms. The scientific problems involved in a resurrection are the restoration of decayed tissue and the renewal of the life previously departed. Presumably, it is no more difficult to God to renew tissue than it is to make it in the first place and apparently the giving or taking of life is His prerogative anyway. In other words, once you recognize God is working, there is no real difficulty left.

[16]"Reproduction, Animal," *Collier's Encyclopedia*, XVI, 666.

The nature miracles involved such things as walking on water, making a huge meal for thousands out of five loaves and two fishes, stilling a storm, withering the leaves of a fig tree, and walking through a closed door. All these things are far beyond our power, but in view of the fact that in Jesus we have the Maker of it all, is such manipulation at all surprising? As science advances, many of the difficulties have a habit of becoming less. Take for instance, the closed door incident. A couple of generations ago, a door was a solid, impassable barrier. Now we know it is mostly space anyway.

There are a considerable number of apostolic miracles too, such as healing, speaking in tongues, miraculous rescues, resurrections, and supernatural enduement with special powers. These are specifically spoken of as the work of the Holy Spirit, and since the Spirit is also God, there is nothing surprising about these miracles either. In some cases in the New Testament, physical processes are involved other than the spoken word. These include such things as laying on of hands, touching the eyelids with spittle, and anointing with oil. However, in some cases such processes were not used, so they probably had no function as healing channels. More likely, they were intended to stimulate faith.

As we come to the end of this chapter on the special difficulties of the Bible, it will have been seen how relatively unimportant the scientific factors are in determining credibility. The critical point is faith in God. If we believe He is in our world in vital action, there is little problem left. However, it is helpful to note that there is nothing in these incidents which is contrary to science even though there is much (as we can expect) which is *beyond* science. Whatever natural processes God used to accomplish His works are only of interest value to us and in most cases as mysterious as ever.

CHAPTER SEVEN

Archaeology

Archaeology is the science which investigates the ruins of ancient civilizations with a view to reconstructing their history and finding out the truth with regard to their customs and ways of living. The science, for all practical purposes, is only about one hundred fifty years old.

The relevance of archaeology to the Bible lies in two directions. First, it is an objective test of the accuracy of the Biblical narrative. Secondly, it provides amplification and light on that narrative. The second purpose of Biblical archaeology is not to be discussed here, for this book is primarily directed to the vindication of the Christian position from a scientific point of view and will, therefore, totally confine its discussion to purpose number one.

In recent years, the reconstruction of ancient history has been solidly based on the objective facts that have come from archaeological research. Before archaeology, it was largely subjective, due to the lack of objective sources of information. Of course, one of the most useful sources was the ancient historians themselves. However, it was not always realized that ancient historians were not guided by the same principles of accuracy that we demand today. Therefore, some of the accounts based upon these ancient historians have been found to be unreliable.

However, much of the story of ancient civilizations was not even discussed by ancient historians. The only resource left to the scholar was to sit down and think out what ancient history must have been like. Obviously, despite the very best intentions in the world, this was a perilous proceeding. Now that objective information has been coming from archaeology, much of this hypothetical history has had to be revised.

This has been particularly true with regard to the reconstructions that have been made of the history that parallels the Biblical accounts. It was assumed by many that the Bible could not have been supernatural; therefore it must be mythical and legendary. It was openly stated that many of the accounts were not written at the time at which they claimed to be and were in fact made in later centuries by forgers. The criterion of this dating is often what these scholars thought the customs and life of these periods must have been.

This analysis of Biblical history is often known as "higher criticism," an unfortunate name because it suggests a negative attitude. The author is grateful that he commenced this study after considerable training in science. After the rigorous methods of science, the procedures here were often appalling. At times the weightiest decisions were found to have been made on the slightest and most trivial grounds. The whole study was littered with assumptions without any substantiation in fact. This, of course, is not true of all scholars, but this subjectivity is so prevalent that you cannot assume the reliability of histories and "introductions" on the Bible. It will take some years before facts and conjectures in this field can be separated.

This criticism caused untold distress to humble Christian people who believed that the Bible was the Word of God and therefore could not be wrong. Yet here were renowned scholars saying it was myth and legend. Unfortunately, it was not possible until recent years to put the whole matter to the acid test.

For a hundred years now, every part of the Bible that could be tested by archaeological discoveries has been put under sharp scrutiny. The results have been so thoroughly convincing that now we look upon archaeology as the most positive evidence that we have for the traditional doctrine of the accuracy of the Scriptures. In almost every area where the Bible was criticized on subjective or theorizing grounds, it has already been vindicated on this objective basis.

The most astounding instance of the power of archaeological testimony was in the experience of William Ramsay.[1]   Just over one hundred years ago, William Ramsay, a young English scholar, went to Asia Minor with the expressed purpose of proving that the history given by Luke in his gospel and in the Acts was inaccurate. His professors had confidently said that Luke could not be right. Ramsay wanted to prove their theories by the evidence of archaeology.

He began to dig in the ancient ruins of Greece and Asia Minor, testing for ancient terms, boundaries, and other items which would be a dead giveaway if a writer had been inventing this history at a later date as claimed. To his amazement, the young student found that the New Testament Scriptures were accurate to the tiniest detail. So convincing was his evidence that Ramsay himself became a Christian and a great Biblical scholar. As a matter of fact, we still look upon Sir William Ramsay's books as being classics so far as the history of the New Testament is concerned.

Since a great deal of archaeological discovery is of recent date, a student should beware of out-of-date books about the Bible. Many of them are based upon the philosophies about ancient histories that have had to be discarded.

It seems clear to the present writer in reading the literature of Christianity which bears on the Bible that a greater amount of Christian scholarship is not yet fully aware of the changes in viewpoint on the historicity of the Bible that have come about as the result of archaeology. A quotation of Dr. Albright, one of

[1]C. M. Cobern, *The New Archaeological Discoveries* (New York: Funk & Wagnalls, 1929), pp. 413, 414.

the most renowned of all archaeologists, is to the point: ". . . The excessive skepticism shown toward the Bible by important historical schools of the eighteenth and nineteenth centuries, certain phases of which still appear periodically, has been progressively discredited. Discovery after discovery has established the accuracy of innumerable details, and has brought increased recognition of the value of the Bible as a source of history."[2]

Much of the archaeological evidence on the authenticity of the Scriptures is related to tiny details which the average person would not notice. Although many of these details are unimportant as far as the general currents of Scriptures are concerned, they do give an opportunity for tests of accuracy. Much of this is especially important with regard to date. A forger or any other person writing centuries after the time that he is pretending to be writing about would trip up on these tiny details.

For instance, critics felt that a later writer had indeed betrayed himself with the story of Abraham because he mentioned such things as camels in Egypt and travel from Mesopotamia to the Mediterranean Sea as occurring round about this time, whereas it was felt that this could not have been true until many years later. But subsequent archaeological discoveries find mention of camels in Egypt long before Abraham's time.[3] And there is on record a contract about a wagon in which it is stated that the lessee agrees not to take it to the Mediterranean Sea.[4] Obviously, this would not have been necessary if such trips had not been possible.

The same kind of detail has been vindicated with regard to the names mentioned in the Joseph narrative.

[2]W. F. Albright, *The Archaeology of Palestine and the Bible* New York: Revell, 1935), p. 127.
[3]Joseph P. Free, "Abraham's Camels," *Journal of Near Eastern Studies* (July, 1944), pp. 187-193.
[4]George A. Barton, *Archaeology and the Bible* (Philadelphia: American Sunday School Union, 1937), p. 293.

If these had been merely the fiction of a later writer, they would not have measured up to the facts. As it happens, the names mentioned in the story of Joseph in the Bible have indeed been found in documents of Egypt dating about that time.[5]

Another instance is the mention of bronze mirrors in Exodus 38:8. It used to be confidently asserted that the later writer had certainly been mistaken with regard to this, because such mirrors would certainly have been unknown at that early date. Subsequent discoveries have shown that there were indeed bronze mirrors in that part of the world about that time.[6]

Sometimes archaeology provides a negative approach. The books of Moses prohibit images of any shape in Hebrew religion. This is a very unusual restriction and completely foreign to normal religious practices. If therefore images of Jehovah had been found, this would have suggested that the Hebrew religion was merely one religion that had evolved among others and did not have a supernatural origin as claimed. Detailed search has never revealed images of this description.[7]

Another instance of this detailed vindication arises from the rather peculiar mention in the story of the destruction of Jericho that Rahab's house was built on the wall, a highly unlikely location. Archaeological discoveries by Garstang[8] on the site of Jericho have shown that there were indeed houses on the wall of that city, possibly because this wall was particularly wide.

Sometimes the evidence does not extend to actual vindication but is corroborative. This is true of the passages in ancient manuscripts which have been discovered which deal with the Creation, the Flood, and

[5]Joseph P. Free, *Archaeology and Bible History* (Wheaton, Illinois: Scripture Press, 1950), p. 77.
[6]*Ibid.,* p. 109.
[7]*Ibid.,* p. 105.
[8]A. Rendle Short, *Modern Discovery and the Bible* (Chicago: Inter-Varsity Press, 1955), p. 155.

other Genesis stories.[9] It is the parallelism here which is of importance to the student because it shows that in many cases long before the Biblical narrative came into being, there was knowledge among ancient peoples of these events of which the Bible speaks.

This is also true with regard to the Levitical laws. It used to be confidently stated that laws of this complexity could not have been possible in primitive days about 1500 B.C. and were therefore the product of a later age. But as a result of a discovery of the tablets of Ras Shamra, we find parallels to these laws of Leviticus which are of even earlier date.[10] Sometimes these parallels are very striking indeed.

Another interesting area in the Old Testament is the history of the Hittites. These people are mentioned many times in the Old Testament as being a very prominent race. At one time it was felt that this was simply not so, that, at the very best, if they existed at all, they could only have been an obscure tribe. However, this picture has completely changed.[11] We now know a great deal about the civilization of the Hittites. Indeed, it is now possible to study their language at some of our great universities.

Even the story of David and his music came under question. It was felt that reference to his starting guilds of musicians in certain directions was definitely wrong because this could not have been possible at that early date. Recent discoveries have shown that this music was in existence many years before David's time.[12]

As far as history is concerned, no area of the Old Testament has come under greater barrage of criticism than that of the book of Daniel. It used to be confidently said that Daniel could not have been written, as

[9]Barton, *op. cit.*, Chapter VII.
[10]Joseph P. Free, "Commentaries from the Clay Tablets — The Ras Shamra Tablets," *Sunday School Times* (April 14, 1945).
[11]"The Hittites," *Encyclopaedia Brittanica* (1957 Edition).
[12]W. F. Albright, *Archaeology and the Religion of Israel* (Baltimore: Johns Hopkins Press, 1942), p. 127.

it claims, around the seventh century, but was instead a concoction which may have been as late as the second century B.C. It was thought that the writer was particularly fouled up when he suggested that the last king of Babylon was killed in an assault on the city and that his name was Belshazzar. Historians had said that Belshazzar never even existed, for Nabonidas was the last king and he was merely captured. It has been shown now that Belshazzar was acting-king.[13] He was the son of Nabonidas who was more or less an absentee king. Belshazzar was indeed slain, just as the Bible says, but Nabonidas remained a captive.

A very interesting and revealing account of how God safeguards the accuracy of His Word is found in Alexander's destruction of Tyre in 332 B.C. Ezekiel, 250 years before, had prophesied this destruction in very explicit terms. Not even the ruins were going to be left, for God was going "... to scrape her dust from her and make her like the top of a rock. It shall be a place for the spreading of nets ..." (Ezekiel 26:4, 5). "They shall lay thy stones and thy timber and thy dust in the midst of the water" (Ezekiel 26:12).

As it turned out,[14] by the time Alexander attacked, the Phoenicians had abandoned the ancient city and taken up residence on an island offshore. To conquer them, Alexander had to construct a causeway from the shore. To do this, he had to scrape up every piece of material from the ancient city and dump it into the water, leaving the ruin so flat and bare that fishermen did indeed, in later years, use it as a place to lay out their nets. They do so even today. Here you have vindication in meticulous detail.

The corroboration of details in the New Testament stories has already been mentioned with regard to the conversion of William Ramsay. These have extended to very insignificant items themselves but which have proved to be a dead give-away with regard

[13]Short, *op. cit.*, p. 195.

[14]Free, *Archaeology and Bible History*, p. 262.

to the facts. Often points of history have been solved, too. For instance, mention of the census in Luke 2:1-3 which has reference to the birth of Jesus has been particularly criticized as being false to the facts known to the ancient historians. Results have now shown that Luke knew what he was talking about and as usual was accurate to the very last letter.[15]

Much discussion has gone on in recent years about the Dead Sea Scrolls, which were discovered in Palestine in 1948. Contrary to some opinions at the time of the discovery, the effect of these scrolls upon the Christian scholarship has not been as great as anticipated. Although some Unitarians have attempted to use them to prove their point against the deity of Christ, their opinions certainly have not been supported by the facts.

But one thing that the Dead Sea Scrolls have done is to strengthen our confidence in the accuracy of those who copied and transmitted the Scriptures. Until the Dead Sea Scrolls were found, our earliest manuscripts of the Old Testament were dated only a thousand years ago, but those of the Dead Sea dated about the time of Christ. Yet in comparing these manuscripts over the gap of one thousand years between them, we notice the discrepancies are very small indeed. This gives evidence that the copyists did their work with the utmost diligence and care. It means that we can be sure that the copy of the Scriptures that we have now is in all essential details identical with the manuscripts as originally written.

The instances cited in this chapter are only a few from among many thousands of cases. The purpose here has been merely to illustrate the kind of contribution to the question of science and religion made by archaeology. The reader will find it a very rewarding study to read a complete book on the subject.

It would be going far beyond the facts at this stage to say that archaeology completely vindicates the

[15]Short, *op. cit.*, p. 210.

historicity and authenticity of the Bible. Actually, all the discoveries that have been made in the areas in which the one touches upon the other are still small in comparison with the total coverage. But the cases of vindication so far are significant because they establish the pattern. If the Bible has been shown to be truthful in these obscure details, it is very unlikely that any part of it is the work of a forger. We can expect that as the years go by there will be further vindication.

CHAPTER EIGHT

Biblical Eschatology and Science

Eschatology is that part of Christian theology which deals with "last things," such as the end of the world and the life to come. We notice that the Bible has some very definite opinions on these subjects, yet the amount of detail is very limited.

This sparsity of detail is not surprising, for if the Biblical position is true, it would be a waste of time for God to give us detail which we would not be able to understand anyway. Our minds are limited by space, time, and matter. In fact, Immanuel Kant taught that time, space, and matter were simply the "categories of the mind," or the framework for thought, rather than being realities in themselves. Modern scientists would not exactly agree with this position but would insist that all human ideas are necessarily expressed in the time-space-matter context.

Yet the world in which God has His being apparently has no such limitations; therefore, the realities of that world cannot be expressed in terms of space, time, and matter which could be understood by us. This seems to be what Paul is referring to when he says, "For now we see through a glass, darkly; but then face to face" (I Corinthians 13:12). For God to attempt to reveal to us in detail the realities of the eternal world would be about as useless as an infant trying to understand the infinitesimal calculus.

What God does reveal to us can only be a pale reflection of the real truth. Language will be strained to the limit. Much of it will have to be figurative rather than absolute. The scientist has an analogous problem when he tries to visualize dimensions beyond the fourth. It is outside immediate experience and therefore cannot be done. In any case, the scientific mind readily agrees that any body of truth is only valid in a certain context. The Biblical claim that the facts of the other world cannot be judged by the conditions of this one is perfectly understandable.

With regard to the end of the world, we notice that the position of the New Testament is clear cut. It does not regard the universe as infinite, but very definitely finite. The whole material universe will be dissolved at a time set by God. ". . . the heavens shall pass away with a great noise, and the elements shall melt with the fervent heat; the earth also and the works therein shall be burned up. Seeing then that all these things shall be dissolved . . ." (II Peter 3:10, 11).

Neither does the Bible agree that mankind is moving towards a utopia when all problems of human behavior will be solved and man will live in perfect peace and happiness. The picture our Lord gives in Matthew 24 and the following chapters is that the end of human history will be a time of terrible distress and evil.

Actually, the problem with such predictions is not with science but with a certain type of humanism which developed a kind of social evolution on the lines of biological evolution. Just as biological evolution assumes a progressive development to more perfect forms of life, so it was felt that human society must be doing the same. Twentieth century disasters have done more to refute this than any intellectual arguments could. The big problem is that human goodness is not inherited. Every child starts from scratch. It may have the advantages of training but advantage of this is often not taken. Indeed, one generation can undo all the good of the past.

Apparently it was the intention of God for this space-time venture to be for a limited period alone. Man's destiny is not intended to be in this earth but in the next world. His sojourn here is simply a preparation for a more infinite life beyond the grave.

There was a time in scientific thought when it was felt that space, time, and matter were infinite and therefore one could expect life upon this earth to go on in unending evolution for all the years to come. This can no longer be believed. The universe is constantly using up energy at a fantastic rate. As many scientists have put it, it is like a clock originally wound up which is steadily running down. In other words, an ultimate end for the universe is certain.

Some modification has been made to this because of nuclear theory. We know now that energy can be created out of matter by the $E = mc^2$ law. Many astronomers feel that this is the source of a great deal of the energy that is being radiated into the universe. But even on this point of view, it is obvious that matter itself must be finite. In other words, there will be an end of the world.

The reference in II Peter to dissolution by intense heat did not have much meaning until recent years. Before atomic energy, it was felt that this was just fantastic imagery which had no correspondence in fact, because we had had no experience of heat which could be quite that destructive. But with the appearance of the atom bomb in 1945, heat comparable to that found in the sun was generated. Those temperatures were so severe that they brought about total dissolution in the immediate vicinity. For instance, the steel towers which held the bombs in the Nevada experiments were completely dissolved. We mentioned before that in the hydrogen bomb experiments in the Pacific, one island, three miles long by one mile wide, completely disappeared. There is no doubt therefore that we have here in the very heart of the atom a power which does have the capacity to destroy the very earth with "fervent heat."

In fact, such explosions do occur every now and again out in space. The astronomers see a flash of a distant world which indicates to them that it has gone out of existence. These are probably nuclear type explosions. Thus discoveries in atomic physics have made the prophecy of II Peter meaningful, whereas before they were open to a great deal of question.

Probably no area of Christian theology has come under greater criticism than the doctrine of resurrection. To many people, it seemed to be utterly fantastic that there could be a perseverance of life after it had been stilled by death and the body had been put into the grave to rejoin the elements from which it came. Many dogmatically said that the spiritual or personality part of man died with his body.

However, this type of pessimism is in itself a contradiction to the conservation law, which insists that nothing can be destroyed, only changed. We know of course that the deceased body is simply changed into other forms of matter, that nothing of the matter is lost. But how can we account for the spiritual or mental characteristics? If these were destroyed, this would entail that the conservation law which is true for the physical things is not true for the mental or spiritual parts of man. In other words, it entails a breakdown of uniformity.

Much of the objections to the Christian doctrine of the resurrection are dependent upon misunderstandings. Paul makes it perfectly clear in I Corinthians 15 and II Corinthians 5 that the body is simply the house of the spiritual part of man which is independent of space, time, and matter and therefore cannot be affected by it. When that house is dissolved, the spiritual part enters the other world of God and takes on a body which he calls a spiritual body. Just as the body upon earth is a space-time-matter body which fits exactly the medium of this world, so the spiritual body of the other world will fit the medium of that world, whatever that happens to be. It emphasizes especially that the spirit in the life to come will not be disembodied. There is no pantheism here. The world to come will be a continuity of personal existence.

This inner life of man is something that goes beyond science. It cannot be proved or disproved by scientists because science, being material, is simply not relevant. But there is nothing unscientific about it. What the Scriptural message seems to say is that these bodies are relative to the space-time-matter continuum in which we live but the inner personality which is immortal is relative to that area outside of space, time, and matter in which God has His being.

As has been mentioned throughout this book, to attempt to prove articles of faith from first principles or from philosophy is simply like a dog chasing his tail. The basis of authority for the Christian must be Jesus Christ. He to us is God Almighty in human flesh; therefore, what He says goes. If we happen to disagree with what He says, it makes no difference to these facts. The earnest Christian in humility simply accepts what Christ says.

This is especially true with regard to the life to come. He Himself by His own resurrection gave us a tremendous vindication for our faith in that He Himself went into that other world to show that such existence was indeed a fact.

The resurrection of Jesus was always one of the most important messages for the early disciples. This was something that to them was based upon fact. According to the New Testament, some five hundred people saw Him after His death (I Corinthians 15:6). These appearances could not have been hallucinations, because they were not by sight or sound alone. People had actually felt Him with their hands, talked with Him, and ate with Him. There could not have been any mistake.

The very change in the disciples' lives is graphic evidence. Before the death of Jesus, they were thoroughly frightened men. After His resurrection, they were willing to go into the streets of Jerusalem accusing those who had put Him to death, knowing that this could bring death to themselves. Now they were completely unafraid of death because He had shown them the way through it.

The connecting link between His conquest of death and ours is our spiritual union with Him which occurs in conversion. Because of this, wherever He is, there we must be also. Already our spiritual roots are in that other world because He is there. We cannot be aware of this because our space-time minds have no capacity for such knowledge. However, when death rends the veil, that other world will be immediately evident to us.

A good analogy of the Biblical doctrine of death is the emergence of the butterfly from the caterpillar stage. In the chrysalis, it puts off the old body and assumes the new with its infinitely greater freedom and beauty.

No one can get any idea of what is going to be the type of existence in the life to come. But human beings, being as they are, have tried to fill this vacuum with their own imagination. Consequently, even now a picture of heaven in most people's minds is one which is more like a fairyland and not too pleasant for our modern minds. The idea of playing harps for all eternity or hacking pieces off the golden streets no longer strikes a responsive chord.

All that can be said here is that the New Testament indicates that the life to come will be a time of greater activity and opportunity than we have ever had before because we will not have with us the limitations of this life. The New Testament picture of God is a dynamic God who is constantly in action. The promise is that we will share in this activity. No grander thought of the future life could ever come to the human mind.

CHAPTER NINE

The Validity of Experience

It has been stated earlier that the history of religious thought in the nineteenth century was one of constant retreat under the onslaughts of the new developments of science. Of course, the great majority of believers allowed the storms to pass over their heads and continued in their traditional faith in the Bible and in the truths of the Christian religion. Many of the more militant conservative theologians carried on a constant and apparently losing war with science.

But liberal theology gave ground continually until, as the twentieth century began, many of them had retreated to the last point of defense, and that was experience. The position was that even if the Bible could no longer be relied upon, the divine origin of man could not be substantiated, and the miracles of the faith had to be abandoned, we still had the refuge of our own hearts which gave us a sense of the presence of God that nothing could take away.

It was this last retreat which came under serious and devastating attack by the rise of psychology as a science in the early part of the present century. Just as other areas of the Christian religion had been explained away in materialistic terms, so also the new science under atheistic and agnostic leadership sought to do the same for spiritual experience.

Looking back from our vantage point now, we can see that the new psychology had an aura of scientific authority which it had no right to claim. Although attempts have constantly been made to put psychology on an objective basis, the subjective element is so strong that whatever is said must always be open to serious revision. In addition, when overenthusiastic thinkers attempted to draw deductions on the existence of God and the validity of conversion, they were going far out of bounds as far as scientific justification was concerned. This type of thinking also suffered from the same kind of error that has been mentioned previously in regard to thought in the physical sciences. Explaining a process which God might use in the realms of mental life does not mean explaining it away. There is no reason to believe that in the realm of the mind God should not use means as He has done elsewhere.

The earliest attack came from the great developments in the psychology of the unconscious under the leadership of Sigmund Freud. The results for the psychoanalytic method as a cure for mental illness were nothing short of amazing. The vast bulk of clinical practice today is still based upon these procedures. The success of the method tended to give a validity to the underlying theory which subsequent thought has not justified.

Briefly, the theory of psychoanalysis is as follows: The inner and outer experiences of life are never forgotten. They are stored up in what is known as the unconscious mind. Many of these experiences are emotionally tinged and remain very lively. They consist of wishes, urges, and propensities which are constantly seeking to find expression in the conscious mind. Dream life is said to be an evidence of this.

This material is prevented from finding conscious fruition by the moral and other inhibitions under which we live. Many of these inner drives, being unable to find satisfaction, become diverted into substitute channels. These substitute channels may lead to abnormal behavior or experiences. Bringing these inner drives to light and finding for them proper recognition and understanding leads the patient back to normal behavior and adjustment. The psychoanalysts themselves vary tremendously on the nature of these unconscious drives, but Freud himself believed them to be fundamentally sexual in nature.

This underlying theory in itself raises no problems for religious thought. The difficulties came with the deductions that were made from it. It was assumed that this was the total explanation of experience, which would mean that a man was not free in his actions even though he thought he was. He was the slave of these unconscious drives. His very beliefs and attitudes were the products of his unconscious mind.

It was openly stated that belief in God was of this nature. It was an attempt to return to the security of childhood when we had a father to protect and lead us by the hand. The Heavenly Father was merely the projection into our conscious minds of this unconscious wish of childhood and therefore had no validity in itself.

On this theory, the religious person was mistaken in assuming that his experience was inspired by the operations of the Holy Spirit within his life. What he was experiencing was simply the stirring of his own unconscious. In particular, it was felt that any intense religious feeling was the sublimation of unsatisfied sexual drive. In evidence of this, cases of medieval women saints were cited because their religious talk was particularly erotic. Some of these people referred to were not only seriously neurotic but possibly even psychotic. Of course, psychology has now moved far away from these attempts to prove theories about normal behavior from the actions of those on the lunatic fringe. But it used to be popular.

One particular area where this kind of teaching was applied was with regard to conversion. Most conversions occur in the teen-age period. It was pointed out that this was the time in life where a young person was developing sexual powers which could not be expressed until later days of marriage. Psychoanalytic thinkers decided, therefore, that this coincidence of conversion and unsatisfied sex was significant and related. Apparently the fact was ignored that this was the most logical time in a person's life for a conscious religious experience to occur anyway, because it is his earliest period of independent thought and experience. The theory also failed to account for the fact that many conversions occur before puberty and although there is a statistical bunching in the teens, conversions do occur throughout life.

In any case, this primacy of the sexual drive has now gone out of fashion, as has also the earlier psychology which considered the personality as the sum total of a great number of separate and distinctive drives. Present theory favors what is sometimes known as the "gestalt approach," which considers the personality as a whole. There is much evidence to show that human behavior is motivated by one primary drive — the expression of the total personality in a satisfying way. Most would now agree that sex is only a minor channel for this great drive.

There seems little doubt that conversion is a triggering of a long process. There is no reason to deny that in most cases a long period of subconscious incubation does go on. Impressions made upon us by our families, Sunday school, church, and our own experiences all lead to the consummation which we refer to as conversion. However, this is only putting in psychological language what the Christian faith teaches anyway, that the Holy Spirit is constantly at work in the human soul. Ultimately the time comes when the sinner, under conviction, cannot reject Christ any longer and then submits to Him in repentance and faith. Usually this experience is climactic, although not necessarily so.

Christianity has no objection to the psychological theory which would suggest that conversion and religious experience are the fruition of certain psychological drives. But we do object when it is claimed that this is all that it is. Our Lord Himself said that He had come to bring life and that more abundantly (John 10:10). It has constantly been the message of our preachers that Christ satisfies. This is true because the experience of conversion and subsequent Christian living is the most satisfying experience that the total personality can find.

It can be seen, therefore, that if much of this psychological theory can be shorn of its excesses, unjustified assumptions, and deductions, instead of a system of knowledge which is contrary to the Christian faith, we find that it supports it.

Perhaps a word ought to be said about the behaviorist cult which started with John Watson during World War I. These psychologists assumed that mental and spiritual phenomena did not exist. They were really an illusion. All behavior, whether overt or experimental, was actually a mechanical process which could be expressed in biological terms. What appeared to be mental was really the smoke that came from these biological fires. It was a completely deterministic system and as such had no place in it for God or for the validity of spiritual experience.

Fortunately now, we do not have to answer this seriously, because it was an outbreak of immaturity in the new science of which we now are not a little bit ashamed. The attempts to classify mental and spiritual experiences under biological terms have failed completely. Nobody knows what is the relationship between mind and body, although it is certain that they are related, as will be seen below. But neither one can be reduced into terms of the other.

Curiously enough in the matter of miracles on healing, both in Biblical times and at the present day, psychology tends to bolster up the Christian position rather than otherwise. This is due largely to the discovery of the tremendous effect of mind over body in the case of the psychophysical or functional diseases.

There are many cases of people who are physically ill or disabled when there are no obvious physical causes at all. The symptoms are just expressions or satisfactions of drives in the unconscious mind. It is found that when upon analysis these underlying causes are brought to light, then the symptoms disappear. That is, there is plenty of evidence of mental factors both causing and curing disease or disablement. This does not mean that all physical ailments have a psychological origin. Many of them obviously do not have, but even cases where the cause of a complaint is obviously physical, the patient's degree of recovery depends tremendously upon his attitude of mind.

People even die because of psychological causes. In the northwest of Western Australia, there is a tribe of aborigines which have a curious form of capital punishment. When a member of a tribe disgraces his people in some offense which is sufficiently serious, the witchdoctor takes the sacred bone and points it at him. The victim then shambles away, drops under the nearest tree, and in a short time is dead. Even in our society in cases of serious illness, if a person loses the will to live, there is very little that medicine can do for him.

To understand what happens in spiritual healing, it must be remembered that the key to all healing is the restorative powers that God has placed within man. The doctor or the drugs do not really cure. All they do is to stimulate into operation these inner powers. The body does the rest. Spiritual or mental factors like prayer and faith do the same kind of thing on a nonphysical basis. They tend to stimulate the same restorative powers into operation. Consequently, spiritual and physical methods are not mutually contradictory. They are complementary in bringing about ultimate healing.

It has been noted that in the gospels our Lord associated sin or forgiveness with healing. Partly because of this, the late Dr. H. L. Fowler of the University of Western Australia used to refer to Jesus as the greatest Psychologist who ever lived. We now know that the removal of guilt from a patient's mind is an important step towards recovery. Our Lord, being God in human flesh, was aware of this long before modern psychology was ever thought of.

These conditions do not mean that all faith healing is valid. Much of the racketeering in faith healing is based upon temporary removal of symptoms by the power of suggestion. Meetings where this occurs are usually marked by a highly charged emotional atmosphere, often with a preacher at the top of his voice calling upon God to heal, as if God were deaf. What this emotionalism usually does is to create a hypnotic atmosphere where suggestion is possible. Under these conditions, people may experience a temporary removal of symptoms, but the failure of these healers to produce substantiated evidence of permanent healing shows that the results are purely temporary. This kind of thing is very unfortunate indeed.

This extravagance should not mislead us into thinking that spiritual healing does not occur. It does. But a hypnotic atmosphere is not necessary. What is of the greatest avail is for the patient to surrender himself to God, accepting from Him the forgiveness of sins. This is true faith. Faith is not merely believing that God is going to heal. This may be impertinent, because God may have other purposes in mind. Faith is the complete committal of the life to God to do with as He wishes. This process often removes barriers of guilt which may have been holding up the cause of healing.

In view of the effect that prayer can have upon a person's mind and body, it would be a very bold psychologist indeed, in our day, to deny its validity or effectiveness. On the other hand we do not know the processes that God uses in response to prayer. Prayer is not a foreign interference in the natural order of things, as some have suggested. It is part of

God's universe, and as such He apparently chooses to use it just as He uses faith, surgery, and the wonder drugs.

The fact that an increasing number of ministers are being trained in psychology is evidence of the fact that this new science is no enemy of the Christian faith. We are still a long way from exhausting the truths of the human mind but we do see as Christians that this kind of understanding can affect the whole of our work to the good. It will enable us to preach our Gospel in a way in which it will have the greatest likelihood of acceptance. It will discover for us more effective methods of teaching, so that the Word of God will be more firmly grounded in the lives of our people. In every way, it is one of God's gifts and can help towards the betterment of mankind.

CONCLUSION

The Future Outlook

The difficulty about writing a book on science and religion is that it can become out of date before it even gets into print. In this book, an attempt to lessen this problem has been made by indicating trends in the various areas which are common to science and religion. Scientists are repeatedly testing their ideas. Change and revision are to be expected always as part of the scientific endeavor. All we can do at any stage is to guess the direction of change and estimate what will be the significance to religion.

The prevailing outlook at the moment appears to be away from a purely materialistic, mechanistic conception of the universe. Of course, the scientific explanation will always have to be in material terms, but the scientist of today no longer claims that this is all there is to the universe. With increasing knowledge, we are farther away than ever from exhausting the secrets of nature. Its depths and recesses are more enshrouded in mystery than ever. Trying to account for things without God is a hopeless task and very few are now attempting it.

As indicated in the Introduction, scientific knowledge is exploding. This is bound to continue with increasing acceleration. More and more scientists will be on the job with increasing funds for research and development. Their efforts will be multiplied beyond belief by the children of their own brains, such as the electronic computer. Incredible amounts of knowledge from every branch of science will be poured into the common hopper. The results cannot but be staggering.

There is nothing in this to cause qualms to the religious man as far as his faith is concerned. For years now the pattern has been clear. Increasing scientific knowledge has brought about greater vindication and understanding of the Christian position. There will inevitably be setbacks. Science has to follow many promising but false trails before it finds the right one. In the end, the secrets of the universe must show the stamp of the Architect who made it, of Him who was expressed in Christ. And He has already spoken in His Word.

There will be many areas of particular interest but the most intriguing of all may well prove to be in the very foundations of science. Already nuclear physics has made startling exceptions to the Law of Uniformity and the Law of Causation. It is obvious that there must be a deeper explanation yet. In any case, the trend is away from explanation on mechanical terms to descriptions by mathematical equations. But what does this mean to the average man? We will have to wait and see, for science is going to appear in a completely different intellectual dress than that of the last hundred years.

Then, one wonders what is going to happen about our understanding of space, time, matter, and energy. We know, of course, that matter and energy are not independent as we used to think. We can connect them by the $E = mc^2$ law, but this gives no clue to the nature of the stuff of which the universe is made. Space and time are not independent either. It has been said that they are related like the two sides of a coin. It is evident that they are neither absolute nor infinite. Will they be shown in the end to be the mere framework of thought without any independent existence, as Kant taught? Even if time is real, as most scientists think, in what way is our universe mixed up in it? Has it always been the same? Some interesting answers are bound to be forthcoming and will be of the utmost importance to the mystery of antiquity.

In astronomy we can expect a settling down period. The last generation has seen a proliferation of short-lived theories on the origin of the planetary system and of the galaxies, the size of the universe and its age. Many of the revisions have been startling — for instance, the recent suggestion that the Palomar telescope may be seeing twice as far as was thought. It is to be hoped that we will get our feet on solid ground in these disputed areas. However, the results will probably be no more than of interpretive value to religion.

There will probably be considerable advance in dating the past by objective methods. The carbon-14 device[1] has already been enormously useful, although it is obvious now that its application is not as foolproof as at first thought. The indirect method by using oxygen-18 to determine ancient temperature trends is interesting and provocative.[2] Undoubtedly there will be other objective methods which will become available. These developments may well settle some of the vexing problems still existing with regard to ancient Biblical history and prehistory.

There is quite a probability that mathematics may help decide some of the disputes on the authorship of certain of the books of the Bible. Some of these questions are critical to the Christian faith, especially where the book claims its own authorship. Obviously, denial of this automatically denies divine inspiration. The author has experimented with this on the Pastoral Epistles (I and II Timothy and Titus) which have been attacked as forgeries. The mathematical treatment based on vocabulary showed a significant likeness of these epistles to those known to be by Paul and a significant difference from other New Testament vocabu-

[1]Willard F. Libby, *Radiocarbon Dating* (Chicago: University of Chicago Press, 1955).
[2]Loren Eiseley, *The Immense Journey* (London: Thames & Hudson, 1957), p. 113.

lary. When perfected, this kind of objective approach could do away with the highly unreliable subjective guesses at present so prevalent in Biblical criticism.

We are more than overdue for some new developments on the relation between living things. So far, the only worked out theory in the field is organic evolution and, as we have seen, this has serious problems. The area where most work needs to be done is in the mechanism of change, for the idea of natural selection is inadequate to explain all the facts. Now that scientists are moving away from the control of materialistic mechanism, it is unlikely that the biological theory will diverge from Christian thought as much as it has in the past.

As to the origin of man, it appears that the evolutionary theory is at a dead end. Since the idea of man as a madeover ape is being abandoned, modern man is left without any known ancestors. On present indications, he appears on the records of the past substantially as he is now. It is difficult to guess as to what leads will be followed up next. If God hasn't changed man since the original creation, the search for ancestors will be fruitless anyway.

There is a great deal of research going on regarding the springs of life. Some scientists are hoping for a breakthrough; others despair of it. It has been for a century one of the most unfruitful fields. The idea of spontaneous generation of entire animals or entire plants has long been vetoed by scientists. Yet some scientists still want to think that life at some submicroscopic level originated by means of spontaneous generation, and some still hope to see it. If it should be found that life is triggered into existence from the inorganic world by some device which we may yet discover, this will be surely another unveiling of the handiwork of the Creator. It will have no negative repercussions for religion, although undoubtedly some would try to use it that way.

It is evident that human life will be prolonged as deathdealing diseases are conquered, but probably not very much. An average hundred-year life span is still a long way off. In any case, we will be merely winning back for ourselves that which is our human birthright, for it is obvious that our years have been whittled away by the ravages of evil. The human body is wonderfully made.

Painstaking archaeological work continues unabated, but the number of breath-taking discoveries is getting fewer and occurring less frequently. As the results are interpreted, we can expect further vindication of the Word of God, but the contribution is likely to be minor as compared with what happened in the past.

The outlook in psychology is saner than it has been in years. It is now highly unlikely that there will be any more widespread defections to such extravagant theories as behaviorism or sex-motivated life. The science is now respectably middle-of-the-road. It looks as if psychiatry is moving away from analysis to synthesis, in which we are more interested in guiding the patient to a more satisfying life than groping in the mazes of the past. This is bringing an enlarged conception of the function of religion in human wellbeing. This is bound to continue and will bring great benefits to both psychology and religion.

We may valiantly hope that the prevailing religious mood of the next generation will be God-centered (theism) rather than man-centered (humanism). In the immediate past, man attempted to explain the universe in terms complimentary to him and especially to science, his brain child. God was vaguely acknowledged but was carefully kept out of the picture. Obviously, tension with personal and revealed religion was inevitable. The bankruptcy of humanism is steadily driving religious thought back to the acknowledgment of God as personally active in the universe. Since this activity reached its pinnacle in the life of Christ, attention is being focused on Him as the basis of authority. This will lead to a more satisfying religion personally and one with an infinitely greater impact upon the life of the day. This is God's answer to the perils of the scientific revolution.

BIBLIOGRAPHY

The list below is only a compendium of references used in this book. The use of a reference does not necessarily mean approval of the book mentioned and this list is not intended as recommended reading.

Adler, Mortimer J.: *What Man Has Made of Man,* New York, Frederick Unger Publishing Co., 1937.

Albright, W. F.: *The Archaeology of Palestine and the Bible,* New York, Revell, 1935.

——: *Archaeology and the Religion of Israel,* Baltimore, Johns Hopkins Press, 1942.

Andrews, R. C.: "Whale," *The World Book Encyclopedia,* Volume 18, 1950 Edition.

Barton, George A.: *Archaeology and the Bible,* Philadelphia, American Sunday School Union, 1937.

Carter, G. S.: *A Hundred Years of Evolution,* New York, The Macmillan Co., 1957.

Cobern, C. M.: *The New Archaeological Discoveries,* New York, Funk & Wagnalls, 1929.

Darwin, Charles: *The Origin of Species,* various editions.

Eiseley, Loren: *The Immense Journey,* London, Thames & Hudson, 1957.

——: *Darwin's Century,* Garden City, New York, Doubleday & Company, Inc., 1958.

Fleming, Ambrose: *Proceedings of the Physical Society,* London, 1914.

Folk, Henry C.: "Reproduction, Animal," *Collier's Encyclopedia,* Volume 16.

Free, J. P.: "Abraham's Camels," *Journal of Near Eastern Studies,* July, 1944.

——: *Archaeology and Bible History,* Wheaton, Illinois, Scripture Press, 1950.

——: "Commentaries from the Clay Tablets — The Ras Shamra Tablets," *Sunday School Times,* April 14, 1945.

Geikie, Cunningham: *Hours With the Bible,* Volume I, New York, James Pott & Co., 1905.

Grebstein, Sheldon N., Editor: *Monkey Trial* (The State of Tennessee vs. John Thomas Scopes), Boston, Houghton Mifflin Company, 1960.

Jung, C. G.: *Modern Man in Search of a Soul,* New York, Harcourt Brace, 1933.

Libby, Willard F.: *Radiocarbon Dating,* Chicago, University of Chicago Press, 1955.

Millikan, Robert Andrew: *Evolution in Science and Religion,* New Haven, Yale University Press, 1935.

Robson, G. C., and Richards, O. W.: *The Variations of Animals in Nature.* Quoted by A. Rendle Short, page 68. See below.

Rush, J. H.: *The Dawn of Life,* Garden City, New York, Hanover House, 1957.

Senet, André: *Man in Search of His Ancestors,* New York, McGraw-Hill Book Co., Inc., 1955.

Short, A. Rendle: *Modern Discovery and the Bible,* Chicago, Inter-Varsity Press, 1955.

Velikovsky, Immanuel, *Ages in Chaos,* Garden City, New York, Doubleday and Co., Inc., 1952.

——: *Worlds in Collision,* New York, The Macmillan Co., 1950.

Weiner, J. S.: *The Piltdown Forgery,* London, Oxford University Press, 1955.

White, Andrew Dickson: *A History of the Warfare of Science With Theology,* Volume I, New York, Appleton, 1922.

Whitman, Howard: *A Reporter in Search of God,* Garden City, New York, Doubleday and Co., Inc., 1953.

Williams, Henry Smith: *Luther Burbank,* London, Grant Richards, Ltd., 1915.

Yutang, Lin: *From Pagan to Christian,* Cleveland and New York, World Publishing Co., 1959.